DISNEY PRINCESS
COMICS TREASURY

JOE BOOKS INC

HarperCollins*PublishersLtd*

Published in the United States by Joe Books
Publisher: Adam Fortier
President: Jody Colero
CEO: Jay Firestone
567 Queen St W, Toronto, ON M5V 2B6
www.joebooks.com

HarperCollins Books may be purchased for educational, business, or sales promotional use through our Special Markets Department.

HarperCollins Publishers Ltd
2 Bloor Street East, 20th Floor
Toronto, Ontario, Canada
M4W 1A8

www.harpercollins.ca

Library and Archives Canada Cataloguing in Publication information is available upon request.

ISBN 978-1-443444-84-2 (HarperCollins Publishers Ltd edition, Canada)
ISBN 978-1-926516-02-8 (Joe Books edition, US)
First Joe Books and HarperCollins Publishers Ltd Editions: January 2015
3 5 7 9 10 8 6 4 2

Printed in USA through Avenue4 Communications at Cenveo/Richmond, Virginia

For information regarding the CPSIA on this printed material, call: (203) 595-3636 and provide reference #RICH - 602286.

TABLE OF CONTENTS

SNOW WHITE AND THE SEVEN DWARFS
Adaptation: Régis Maine
Pencils: Santiago Barreira
Inks: Comicup Studio
Letters: Erika Terriquez

TANGLED
Adaptation: Alessandro Ferrari
Layout: Elisabetta Melaranci
Clean-Up (Characters): Elisabetta Melaranci
Clean-Up (Backgrounds): Emilio Grasso, Luca Usai
Inks: Cristina Giorgilli, Francesco Abrignani
Color: Angela Capolupo, Mara Damiani, Giuseppe Fontana
Additional Contributors: Elisa Checchi, Elisabetta Sedda, Bryce Vankooten

THE LITTLE MERMAID
Adaptation: Tom Anderson
Pencils: Xavier Vives Mateu
Letters: Bill Spicer
Color: Jo Meugniot

BEAUTY AND THE BEAST: TIME FLIES
Story: Howard Mackie
Pencils: Steven Butler
Inks: Jim Amash

SNOW WHITE: SNOW PROBLEM!
Story: Sheryl Scarborough and Kayte Kuch
Pencils: George Wildman
Inks: Steve George

ALADDIN: FLYING CARPET TRAFFIC
Story: Evert Geradts
Translation: David Gerstein
Pencils: Carmen Pérez
Inks: Comicup Studio
Letters: David Gerstein
Color: Sanoma

THE PRINCESS AND THE FROG
Adaptation: Augusto Macchetto
Layout: Elisabetta Melaranci
Clean-Up: Elisabetta Melaranci, Luca Usai
Inks: Cristina Giorgilli
Color: Andrea Cagol, Giuseppe Fontana, Kawaii Creative Studio, Alisa Schmuhl, Helge Vogt
Additional Contributors: Silvia Cassinari, Flavio Chiumento, Marta De Cunto, Michela Frare, Fabio Salvitto, Elisabetta Sedda

ALADDIN
Adaptation: Bobbi J.G. Weiss
Pencils: Xavier Vives Mateu
Inks: Jaime Diaz Studio, Josep Tello Gonzalez, Xavier Vives Mateu
Letters: Bill Spicer
Color: Carl Gafford

THE LITTLE MERMAID: SERPENT TEEN
Story: Peter David
Pencils: Chuck Austen, Bill Fugate
Inks: Dave Hunt, Lea Hernandez
Letters: Gaspar Saladino
Color: Jo Meugniot

SLEEPING BEAUTY
Adaptation: Régis Maine
Pencils: Mario Cortes
Inks: Comicup Studio
Letters: Erika Terriquez

MULAN
Adaptation: Bob Foster, Greg Ehrbar
Pencils: Mario Cortes
Inks: Comicup Studio
Letters: Erika Terriquez

THE LITTLE MERMAID: SCUTTLE IN "CULINARY CUT-UPS"
Story: Peter David

Pencils: Mark Marderosian
Inks: Brian Garvey
Letters: Gaspar Saladino
Color: Jo Meugniot

CINDERELLA
Adaptation: Régis Maine
Pencils: Mario Cortes
Inks: Comicup Studio
Letters: Erika Terriquez

ALADDIN: THE RETURN OF JAFAR
Adaptation: Régis Maine
Translation: David Gerstein
Pencils: Carmen Pérez
Inks: Comicup Studio
Letters: Erika Terriquez
Color: Chagnaud

THE LITTLE MERMAID: ERIC MEETS HER HIGHNESS
Story: Peter David
Pencils: Dan Gracey
Inks: Dave Hunt
Letters: Gaspar Saladino
Color: Jo Meugniot

MULAN: THE MIGHTY DRAGON
Story: Carson Van Osten
Pencils: Paulo Borges
Inks: Antônio De Lima
Letters: Gaspar Saladino
Color: N. Yoshikawa And D. Amorim

BEAUTY AND THE BEAST
Adaptation: Bobbi J.G. Weiss
Pencils: Colleen Doran
Inks: Dave Hunt
Letters: Todd Klein
Color: Jo Meugniot

THE LITTLE MERMAID: GUPPY LOVE
Story: Peter David
Pencils: Scott Benefiel
Inks: Dave Hunt
Letters: Gaspar Saladino
Color: Jo Meugniot

BRAVE
Adaptation: Alessandro Ferrari
Layouts: Emilio Urbano
Pencils: Manuela Razzi
Color: Giuseppe Fontana, Massimo Rocca, Angela Capolupo

POCAHONTAS
Adaptation: Bob Foster
Art: Dan Spiegle
Letters: Erika Terriquez

BEAUTY AND THE BEAST: BEWITCHED, BOTHERED, AND BEWILDERED
Plot: Cris Palomino and Karen Kreider ("Bewitched" and

"Bewildered"), John Blair Moore ("Bothered")
Script: John Blair Moore
Pencils: Cosme Quartieri, Jorge Sanchez, Wanda Gattino
Inks: Raul Barbéro, Raul Torreiro, Robert Bat, Rubén Torreiro
Letters: Gaspar Saladino
Color: Jo Meugniot

CINDERELLA'S CHRISTMAS PARTY
Story: Frank Reilly
Pencils: Floyd Gottfredson
Inks: Manuel Gonzales
Letters: David Gerstein, Floyd Gottfredson

THE LITTLE MERMAID: THE HUNT FOR THE REDHEAD DOWN UNDER
Story: Peter David
Pencils: Bill Fugate
Inks: Dave Hunt
Letters: Gaspar Saladino
Color: Jo Meugniot

MULAN: THE DANCING HORSE
Story: Bob Foster, Carson Van Osten
Pencils: Gustavo Machado
Inks: Antônio De Lima
Letters: Gaspar Saladino
Color: Alexandre Silva

BEAUTY AND THE BEAST: ELSEWHERE AND ELSEWHEN
Story: John Blair Moore
Art: Jorge Sanchez
Letters: Gaspar Saladino
Color: Jo Meugniot

ALADDIN AND THE KING OF THIEVES
Adaptation: Didier Le Bornec
Translation: David Gerstein
Pencils: Carmen Pérez
Inks: Comicup Studio
Letters: Erika Terriquez
Color: Chagnaud

SNOW WHITE: GRUMPY BIRTHDAY TO YOU!
Story: Trina Robbins
Pencils: Gonzalo Mayo
Inks: Steve George

THE LITTLE MERMAID: THE CHRISTMAS SPIRIT
Story: Giuseppe Ramello
Translation: David Gerstein
Art: Francesco Legramandi
Letters: Erika Terriquez

THANKS TO DAVID GERSTEIN FOR HIS IMPECCABLE RESEARCH, UNERRING GOOD TASTE, AND INVALUABLE ASSISTANCE. SPECIAL THANKS TO JULIE DORRIS, CURT BAKER, TERI AVANIAN, CHARLENE PUGH, ARIANNA MARCHIONE, AND THE REST OF THE DISNEY PUBLISHING WORLDWIDE COMICS TEAM.

COLLECTION EDITOR: JESSE POST
DESIGNER: ERIKA TERRIQUEZ

ONCE UPON A TIME, IN A FAR OFF LAND, THERE WAS A CASTLE LIKE THOSE FOUND ONLY IN DREAMS AND FAIRY TALES...

SnowWhite
and the Seven Dwarfs

...AND IN THIS CASTLE LIVED A QUEEN...

...WHOSE STRIKING BEAUTY...

...WAS MATCHED ONLY BY HER WICKEDNESS...

MIRROR, MIRROR, ON THE WALL...

...WHO IS THE FAIREST OF THEM ALL?

EVERY DAY THE MIRROR GAVE THE SAME ANSWER, UNTIL...

O, MY QUEEN...

...UNTIL NOW, YOUR BEAUTY WAS ALWAYS UNSURPASSED...

...BUT NOW THERE IS SOMEONE ELSE...

...WHOSE FEATURES ARE PERFECT...

...WHOSE EYES ARE ADORABLE, AND WHOSE...

ENOUGH! HER NAME! I MUST KNOW HER NAME!

IT IS THE PRINCESS SNOW WHITE, MY QUEEN.

SO, ENRAGED BY THE MIRROR'S REPLY, THE WICKED STEPMOTHER GAVE SNOW WHITE ALL THE HARDEST WORK TO DO...

...BUT NOTHING COULD CHANGE SNOW WHITE'S HAPPY NATURE...

ISN'T THE WEATHER BEAUTIFUL TODAY, LITTLE BIRD?

AND WHAT DO YOU THINK OF MY PRETTY DRESS?

♪ ♪ ♪ ♪

I WILL WEAR IT TONIGHT WHEN I DANCE AT THE BALL WITH MY PRINCE!

THIS LIFE WILL NOT LAST FOREVER. ONE DAY, MY PRINCE WILL COME AND RESCUE ME!

LET'S GO DOWN TO THE WELL TO MAKE A WISH. I AM SURE IT WILL COME TRUE.

I WISH, I WISH THAT MY PRINCE WILL FIND THE PATH LEADING TO THIS CASTLE!

PRINCE CASTLE

OH!

AND SO, SOON AFTERWARDS...

YOU SENT FOR ME, YOUR MAJESTY?

YES, COME IN, HUNTSMAN.

HOW MAY I SERVE YOUR MAJESTY?

I COMMAND YOU TO TAKE SNOW WHITE INTO THE FOREST...

...FIND A DESOLATE CLEARING...

...AND *KILL* HER!

NO! YOUR MAJESTY, *I COULDN'T!*

OBEY ME, OR I WILL KILL YOU *AND* YOUR FAMILY.

-SIGH- AS YOU COMMAND, YOUR MAJESTY.

AND AS PROOF OF HER DEATH...

...YOU MUST BRING BACK HER *HEART* TO ME IN THIS BOX!

SADDENED BY HIS TERRIBLE TASK, THE HUNTSMAN TOOK SNOW WHITE DEEP INTO THE FOREST...

I WOULD BE SCARED IF YOU WERE NOT HERE WITH ME, BUT WITH YOU, I KNOW I AM SAFE.

WHAT A WONDERFUL DAY.

ER, YES, ER...

YOU DO NOT SEEM VERY HAPPY. ARE YOU IN TROUBLE?

NO, SNOW WHITE, NO, BUT...

OH, *LOOK!*

A LOST BIRD.

DO NOT CRY, LITTLE BIRD. I WILL HELP YOU FIND YOUR PARENTS AGAIN.

SEE, THERE THEY ARE.

WHAT IS THE MATTER, LITTLE ONE?

TERRIFIED, SNOW WHITE FLED DEEPER AND DEEPER INTO THE FOREST...

...EVEN THE TREES WERE LIKE FRIGHTENING MONSTERS...

...TRYING TO GRAB HER...

...AND IN THE SHADOWS, HUNDREDS OF EYES SEEMED TO BE WATCHING AS...

...SHE FELL INTO A MUDDY POND...

...AND IMAGINED THERE WERE CROCODILES, WAITING OPEN-MOUTHED, TO EAT HER...

...DRAGGING HERSELF FROM THE MUD, SHE RAN ON AGAIN...

...BUT SHE COLLAPSED...

...EXHAUSTED!

THE NEXT MORNING...

NO, *NO!* PLEASE DON'T KILL ME!

OH!

WAIT! DON'T GO AWAY!

I AM AS AFRAID AS YOU ARE.

THE FOREST MUST BE MY HOME FROM NOW ON. BUT WHERE SHALL I FIND A HOUSE HERE?

MAYBE YOU KNOW OF ONE?

YOU WANT ME TO FOLLOW YOU? IS THAT IT?

AND SO, SNOW WHITE'S NEW FRIENDS LED HER TO A NEW PART OF THE FOREST...

...WHICH, AS A NEW DAY DAWNED, SEEMED LESS FRIGHTENING THAN BEFORE.

THEN, AT THE EDGE OF A CLEARING...

OH, LOOK!

SNOW WHITE COULD HARDLY BELIEVE HER EYES...

WHY, IT'S JUST LIKE A DOLL'S HOUSE!

17

WHO COULD POSSIBLY LIVE IN THIS COTTAGE?

IT SEEMS TO BE EMPTY.

WHAT TINY FURNITURE! AND WHAT A MESS!

PERHAPS THERE ARE CHILDREN LIVING HERE?

WHOEVER IT IS NEEDS A LESSON IN TIDINESS!

THERE, I'VE CLEANED IT ALL UP! NOW, LET'S LOOK UPSTAIRS.

DOC? GRUMPY? SNEEZY? WHAT FUNNY NAMES!

MEANWHILE, IN ANOTHER PART OF THE FOREST...

HURRY, *HURRY!* THE DAY IS COMING TO AN END!

WE'LL HAVE TO WORK HARDER! WE MUST GET MORE JEWELS OUT OF THIS MINE. SO FAR WE ONLY HAVE...

...FIVE TONS OF DIAMONDS.

...THREE TONS OF RUBIES...

...FOUR TONS OF EMERALDS, AND...

PAH! ISN'T THAT ENOUGH? *HUH?*

LET'S TALK ABOUT THIS WHILE WE ROAM. HMM, I MEAN, LET'S TALK ABOUT THIS AT *HOME!*

IN THE COTTAGE, SNOW WHITE WAS FAST ASLEEP AMONG HER FOREST FRIENDS...

...WHEN SUDDENLY...

...THE ANIMALS SENSED THE DWARFS APPROACHING THEIR COTTAGE...

SO, THEY RAN DOWN THE STAIRS...

...AND OUT OF THE HOUSE...

...JUST IN TIME!

C-C-C-COURAGE, MEN!

GOOD GRIEF! IT'S A *HUGE* MONSTER!

SSH! DON'T MAKE A SOUND!

HUSH UP!

EVERYONE SURROUND IT!

GET READY NOW! WE MUST ALL STRIKE AT THE SAME TIME...

...ONE, TWO...

WATCH OUT, IT'S MOVING!

OH, *MY!*

DON'T PAY ANY ATTENTION TO WHAT GRUMPY SAYS. HE DOESN'T LIKE PEOPLE VERY MUCH!

HE LOOKS RATHER CUTE, THOUGH!

SHE'S A FLATTERER, TOO! *POUGH!* ASK HER WHAT SHE'S DOING HERE!

AH, YES! WHAT *ARE* YOU DOING HERE, MY DEAR?

I NEEDED SOMEWHERE TO SLEEP. MY NAME'S SNOW WHITE. I RAN AWAY FROM MY STEPMOTHER, THE QUEEN. SHE WANTED TO...

THE QUEEN?!

YOU MUST LEAVE US, SNOW WHITE, OR THE QUEEN WILL KILL US ALL!

WE CAN'T TURN THIS POOR CHILD OUT.

SHE'S ALL BAD NEWS -- SHE MUST *GO!*

I BEG YOU, PLEASE LET ME STAY!

THE QUEEN WILL FIND YOU WHEREVER YOU ARE. SHE'S A TERRIBLE WITCH.

SHE CAN MAKE HERSELF INVISIBLE.

SHE MAY ALREADY BE HERE!

D-D-DON'T BE TOO HASTY! I'M SURE THE Q-QUEEN DOESN'T KNOW WHERE SHOW WHITE IS!

BUT, AT THAT VERY MOMENT...

MIRROR, MIRROR ON THE WALL. WHO IS THE FAIREST OF THEM ALL?

THE FAIREST IS SNOW WHITE. SEARCH FOR HER IN THE FOREST! SHE HAS FLED TO THE COTTAGE OF THE SEVEN DWARFS!

YOU LIE! SHE'S DEAD! HER HEART IS IN THIS BOX!

NO, MY QUEEN. THE HUNTSMAN LIED TO YOU! THE HEART OF AN ANIMAL IS IN THAT BOX.

AAAAAAAAAHH!!!!

DEEP INTO THE NIGHT, THE DWARFS ARGUED. SHOULD SNOW WHITE STAY... OR SHOULD SHE GO?

I SAY WE GET RID OF HER. THE QUEEN IS BOUND TO FIND OUT SHE'S HERE!

I THINK SHE SHOULD STAY! LET'S TAKE A VOTE ON IT!

WHO VOTES FOR HER TO STAY?

ME! ME! ME!

NO! NO!

PLEASE DON'T FIGHT OVER ME. I'LL GO...

...OF COURSE, IF I STAYED, I WOULD MEND YOUR CLOTHES, CLEAN YOUR COTTAGE...

PAH! IT'S ALREADY CLEAN!

...AND I WOULD COOK FOR YOU.

COOK? COOK WHAT?

MEAT PIES! APPLE TARTS! CHOCOLATE CAKES! ANYTHING YOU LIKE!

HOORAY!!

ALL RIGHT! YOU'RE ALL MAD! SHE'LL BRING US NOTHING BUT TROUBLE, YOU'LL SEE!

IN HER CASTLE, THE QUEEN WAS PREPARING AN EVIL, MAGIC POTION...

SOME SKELETON DUST, TO MAKE ME *OLDER*...

...AN OLD WOMAN'S COUGH TO BREAK MY VOICE...

...A *HOWL OF TERROR*, TO MAKE MY HAIR WHITE, AND...

...ONE DRINK OF THIS MAGIC BREW -- THEN I WILL BE SO TRANSFORMED, SNOW WHITE WILL *NEVER* RECOGNIZE ME!

HOW DO I LOOK, MY PRECIOUS ONE?

AAAAHHH!

CAW! CAW!

CROAK! UURGH!

DID I SCARE YOU, MY LITTLE ONE?

BRILLIANT! BRILLIANT! I DON'T EVEN RECOGNIZE MYSELF! HEH-HEH-HEH!

NOW, LET'S FIND A PRESENT FOR LITTLE SNOW WHITE.

"THE APPLE OF ETERNAL SLEEP." THAT'S *EXACTLY* WHAT I NEED!

BACK IN THE COTTAGE OF THE SEVEN DWARFS, A PARTY WAS IN FULL SWING...

OH! I'M SO HAPPY. IT'S WONDERFUL TO HAVE SUCH GOOD FRIENDS...

...AND NOW I WOULD LIKE TO TELL YOU ALL ABOUT MY PRINCE...

...YOU SEE, I THINK OF HIM EVERY SINGLE MINUTE OF EVERY SINGLE DAY, AND I'M SURE HE'S THINKING OF ME, TOO! ONE DAY WE SHALL BE TOGETHER -- FOREVER!

OH, MY! LOOK HOW LATE IT IS! TIME FOR BED!

NO, IT'S TOO LATE. YOU MUST GO UPSTAIRS TO BED!

JUST ONE MORE DANCE, SNOW WHITE?

HUM! DEAR PRINCESS, WE'VE DECIDED TO SLEEP DOWN HERE. WE'LL BE FINE. YOU MAY HAVE OUR BEDS.

OH, YOU'RE SO KIND! THANK YOU ALL, AND SWEET DREAMS!

AND SO, THE SILENCE OF SLEEP FELL OVER THE DWARFS' COTTAGE...

BUT ELSEWHERE...

HEH-HEH! WHAT'S TASTIER THAN A BIG, RED, JUICY APPLE?

INTO THE CAULDRON YOU GO...

...AND WHEN SNOW WHITE BITES YOU, HER BLOOD WILL TURN TO ICE...

...SHE WILL STOP BREATHING, AND SHE WILL FALL ASLEEP *FOREVER!*

WHO WILL SUSPECT AN ORDINARY APPLE TAKEN AT RANDOM FROM A BASKET?

BUT WAIT...

...PERHAPS THERE'S AN ANTIDOTE TO THIS SPELL?

YES, THERE IS! A THOUSAND CURSES! WHAT DOES IT SAY?

"A KISS OF TRUE LOVE HAS THE POWER TO BRING THE VICTIM BACK FROM THE EVIL SPELL, AND RETURN THEM TO THE WORLD OF THE LIVING."

AAAAHH!

I KNEW IT!

BUT I WOULD BE STUPID TO WORRY ABOUT SUCH A LITTLE THING...

...BECAUSE SNOW WHITE WILL STOP BREATHING AND THE DWARFS WILL BELIEVE SHE IS DEAD!

HEH-HEH-HEH!

IT'S TIME TO LEAVE...

...I DON'T WANT TO KEEP MY LITTLE PRINCESS WAITING!

OH, ARE YOU THIRSTY, MY LITTLE ONE?

THEN HELP YOURSELF!

HEH-HEH-HEH!!

THE WITCH LEFT THE CASTLE USING A SECRET PASSAGE...

...WHICH CAME OUT IN THE MIDDLE OF THE FOREST...

SOON, AS THE SUN ROSE OVER THE DWARFS' COTTAGE...

...IT WAS TIME FOR THEM TO GO TO WORK IN THE MINE...

AND ABOVE ALL, DON'T LET *ANYONE* IN, SNOW WHITE. THE QUEEN IS CAPABLE OF *ANYTHING!*

DON'T WORRY, DOC!

HUM! ER, YES, OF COURSE!

PAH! LOOK AT THAT. *ERGH!*

~GULP~ GOODBYE, SNOW WHITE.

NOW, BE VERY CAREFUL!

OH, GRUMPY! ARE YOU WORRIED ABOUT ME?

BYE, MY SWEET, LITTLE GRUMPY.

YEOW!

HI-HO! HI-HO! IT'S OFF TO WORK WE GO! HI-HO!

HEH-HEH! THE DWARFS ARE GONE. SNOW WHITE IS ALL ALONE!

AND INSIDE THE HOUSE...

MY FRIENDS, WE WILL GIVE GRUMPY A BIG SURPRISE TONIGHT!

WE WILL MAKE HIM A CHOCOLATE CAKE!

NO, WAIT! AN APPLE PIE WOULD BE BETTER.

LET'S ROLL THE DOUGH CAREFULLY.

WAIT! I THINK I'M MISSING SOMETHING...

COULD IT BE THE APPLES? HEH-HEH!

OH!

IT'S ALL RIGHT, MY CHILD. I'M ONLY A POOR OLD BEGGAR WOMAN!

GO AWAY! LET GO OF HER!

GO AWAY! *GO AWAY!*

SENSING THE DANGER, THE ANIMALS FLED TO WARN THE DWARFS...

OF COURSE!

OH, MY HEART! MAY I COME IN TO REST A MOMENT?

THERE! PLEASE SIT DOWN!

OH, YOU'RE SO BEAUTIFUL AND KIND!

LET ME REWARD YOU FOR YOUR KINDNESS...

...HERE, TAKE A BITE OF THIS JUICY APPLE, AND TELL ME WHAT YOU THINK! HEH-HEH!

MEANWHILE, THE ANIMALS ARRIVED AT THE MINE...

WHAT'S ALL THIS ABOUT?

WHAT DO YOU WANT?

THEY'VE GONE CRAZY!

I DON'T UNDERSTAND IT.

GO AWAY!

GOODNESS ME! I KNOW WHAT'S HAPPENING...

...THEY'RE TRYING TO TELL US SOMETHING ABOUT SNOW WHITE!

SNOW WHITE? YOU MEAN, SHE MAY BE IN DANGER?

QUICK! BACK TO THE COTTAGE!

BUT...

COME ALONG, DEAR! DON'T BE SHY! JUST A TINY BITE.

GO ON! MY APPLES ARE SO TASTY! THERE AREN'T ANY BETTER APPLES IN THE WORLD.

WELL, IT DOES LOOK VERY NICE.

FASTER! FASTER!

THERE! IT'S GOOD, ISN'T IT? WHAT DO YOU THINK?

AAAAHH!

YES, THAT'S IT!

YOUR BLOOD WILL TURN TO ICE! YOU WILL STOP BREATHING..

...AND THE SPELL WILL DO ITS TERRIBLE WORK.

PRETTY LITTLE SNOW WHITE IS NO LONGER A RIVAL TO MY BEAUTY...

...I HAVE WON! HEH-HEH!

FROM NOW ON, I AM THE FAIREST OF THEM ALL! ~CACKLE~ ~CACKLE~

MY VICTORY IS COMPLETE!

BUT WAIT! WHAT'S THAT NOISE?

CURSES! IT'S THOSE PESKY *DWARFS!*

I'LL GET REVENGE ON THEM LATER, BUT NOW I MUST FLEE.

LOOK! THERE SHE IS!

THE WITCH! SHE'S RUNNING AWAY!

AFTER HER!

THE LITTLE BEASTS, THEY'RE *GAINING* ON ME.

I'LL TAKE A SHORTCUT THROUGH THE MOUNTAINS.

BACK HOME, THE DWARFS DISCOVER SNOW WHITE LYING LIFELESS...

DEAD! I DON'T BELIEVE IT!

SHE LOOKS LIKE AN ANGEL!

I CAN'T BELIEVE WE'LL NEVER SEE HER SING AND DANCE AGAIN!

YOU'RE RIGHT! IT IS UNBEARABLE. BUT I HAVE AN IDEA! LISTEN!

AN *IDEA*? WHAT *SORT* OF IDEA?

WE'LL BUILD A CRYSTAL TOMB FOR HER. THEN WE WILL BE ABLE TO WATCH OVER HER FOREVER!

AND SO IT WAS DONE...

THEN, ONE DAY, SNOW WHITE'S PRINCE HAPPENED TO RIDE PAST THAT FAR CORNER OF THE FOREST...

IT WAS A MIRACLE! THE KISS OF TRUE LOVE BROKE THE EVIL SPELL...

HOORAY! SHE'S ALIVE!

DEAR SNOW WHITE, THIS IS THE MOST WONDERFUL DAY OF MY LIFE!

Once upon a time, a single drop of sunlight fell from the heavens.

Tangled

FROM THIS SMALL DROP OF SUN...

...GREW A **MAGICAL GOLDEN FLOWER**, WITH THE POWER TO HEAL THE SICK AND INJURED.

NEARBY, WAS A GLORIOUS KINGDOM.

THE KINGDOM WAS RULED BY THE MOST GENEROUS KING AND QUEEN, WHO WERE SOON TO HAVE A BABY.

BUT THE QUEEN BECAME VERY SICK. THE ENTIRE KINGDOM KNEW THE LEGEND OF THE MAGICAL FLOWER: AT ONCE, THEY LAUNCHED A SEARCH.

THE FLOWER, CENTURIES EARLIER, HAD BEEN DISCOVERED BY A VAIN OLD WOMAN: **MOTHER GOTHEL**.

SHE HOARDED ITS HEALING POWER AND USED IT INSTEAD TO KEEP HER YOUNG.

UNTIL, ONE DAY, A ROYAL GUARD FINALLY FOUND IT.

A POTION WAS MADE AND FED TO THE QUEEN. MIRACULOUSLY, SHE WAS HEALED.

A HEALTHY BABY GIRL, A PRINCESS, WAS BORN WITH BEAUTIFUL GOLDEN HAIR.

TO CELEBRATE HER BIRTH, THE KING AND QUEEN LAUNCHED A FLYING LANTERN INTO THE SKY. BUT THEIR HAPPINESS WAS SHORT-LIVED...

...FOR A VENGEFUL MOTHER GOTHEL BROKE INTO THE CASTLE, LOOKING FOR THE FLOWER'S MAGIC.

SHE FOUND IT, BUT SHE ALSO FOUND OUT...

FZAC

...IT WAS IMPOSSIBLE TO SEPARATE THE MAGIC FROM THE BABY!

SO MOTHER GOTHEL STOLE THE CHILD AND VANISHED.

THE KINGDOM COULD NOT FIND THE PRINCESS.

FOR DEEP INSIDE THE FOREST, IN A **HIDDEN TOWER...**

...GOTHEL RAISED THE CHILD AS HER OWN. THE CHILD'S HAIR CONTINUED TO RESTORE HER YOUTH AND BEAUTY. SHE CHERISHED RAPUNZEL, BUT KEPT HER IN SOLITUDE.

WHY CAN'T I GO OUTSIDE?

THE OUTSIDE WORLD IS A DANGEROUS PLACE, RAPUNZEL. YOU MUST STAY HERE, WHERE YOU'RE SAFE.

YES, MOMMY.

BUT NOTHING COULD CONTAIN THE HOPEFUL SPIRIT OF A PRINCESS.

EACH YEAR ON HER BIRTHDAY, THE KING AND QUEEN RELEASED THOUSANDS OF LANTERNS, IN THE HOPE THAT ONE DAY THEIR LOST PRINCESS WOULD RETURN.

EACH YEAR RAPUNZEL WATCHED THEM WITHOUT KNOWING IT...

MANY YEARS LATER, IN THE SAME TOWER...

JUST 24 HOURS TILL MY BIRTHDAY! ONE DAY AND I'LL BE 18!

A DAY I GUESS WILL BE SPENT LIKE THE LAST 6,000 I'VE SEEN... GOOD MORNING, PASCAL!

OUT OF THE TOWER?

OH, COME ON, IT'S NOT THAT BAD HERE...

I'LL START WITH THE CHORES! SWEEP, POLISH AND WAX, DO LAUNDRY, DUST, MOP AND SHINE UP...THEN SWEEP AGAIN!

FRUSCH

FRUSCH

THEN I'LL READ A BOOK... OR MAYBE TWO OR THREE.

I'LL ADD A FEW NEW PAINTINGS TO MY GALLERY...

...AND I'LL BRUSH AND BRUSH AND BRUSH MY HAIR. AND THEN... THEN...

...AND THEN, AT DUSK, THE LIGHTS WILL APPEAR, JUST LIKE EVERY BIRTHDAY

AND I'LL KEEP WONDERING WHEN WILL MY LIFE BEGIN? WHEN MOTHER WILL LET ME GO?

RAPUNZEL! LET DOWN YOUR HAIR!

UH, MOTHER!

OKAY, I'M JUST GONNA DO IT. I'LL ASK HER TO LET ME...LET...

RAPUNZEL! I'M NOT GETTING ANY YOUNGER, DOWN HERE...

"COME ON, PASCAL! DON'T LET HER SEE YOU."

HOW DO YOU MANAGE TO DO THAT EVERYDAY, IT LOOKS ABSOLUTELY EXHAUSTING!

OH, IT'S NOTHING.

THEN I DON'T KNOW WHY IT TAKES SO LONG.

OH, I'M JUST TEASING. I LOVE YOU SO MUCH. HAHA!

SO, HEM...MOTHER. AS YOU KNOW, TOMORROW I'LL TURN 18 AND I WAS HOPING YOU WOULD TAKE ME TO SEE THE FLOATING LIGHTS!

WHAT?

I NEED TO SEE THEM, MOTHER. AND NOT JUST FROM MY WINDOW...IN PERSON!

GO OUTSIDE? WHY, RAPUNZEL...

NOT FAR FROM THERE...

LOOK AT THIS!

WANTED
DEAD or ALIVE
Flynn Rider
THIEF

IS IT TOO MUCH TO ASK TO GET MY NOSE RIGHT?

THERE!

WANTED
DEAD or ALIVE
THIEF

THERE THEY ARE!

THE ROYAL GUARDS! RUN, GUYS!

OKAY, GIVE ME A BOOST AND THEN I'LL PULL YOU UP.

GIVE US THE **SATCHEL** FIRST...

WHAT?

I CAN'T BELIEVE THAT AFTER ALL WE'VE BEEN THROUGH TOGETHER...

STOP IT! GIVE ME THA...!

SWISH

?!

CRACK

THIS IS YOUR FAULT! BAD HORSE, BAD...

BAM!

FLYNN AND THE HORSE FALL IN THE CANYON BELOW, AND WHEN THEY LAND...

SNIFF SNIFF

...FLYNN FINDS A WAY TO ESCAPE!

?

A CAVE?!

THE HORSE IS STILL THERE, STILL SEARCHING FOR HIM...

WOW!

...SO THERE'S NO CHOICE FOR FLYNN!

ALONE, AT LAST!

PANG

OH, OH... AND NOW?

THUMP

!

RAPUNZEL HIDES THE STRANGER...

OKAY... YOU... STAY... THERE!

I WILL SHOW MOM HOW I SORTED HIM OUT. SHE'LL UNDERSTAND I CAN GO OUTSIDE!

AND YOU?

WOW!

WHEN MOTHER GOTHEL RETURNS, RAPUNZEL HAS HIDDEN THE CATCHEL, TOO. SHE WANTS TO PROVE SHE CAN GO OFF ON HER OWN, BUT...

I'VE BEEN THINKING ABOUT WHAT YOU SAID EARLIER AND...

I HOPE YOU'RE NOT STILL TALKING ABOUT THE STARS, SWEETHEART.

YOU'RE **NEVER** LEAVING THIS TOWER. **EVER.**

DEEPLY DISAPPOINTED, RAPUNZEL FINDS A NEW WAY TO MAKE HER DREAM COME TRUE...

I...I JUST KNOW WHAT I WANT FOR MY BIRTHDAY, MOTHER. THE PAINT MADE FROM THE WHITE SHELLS YOU ONCE BROUGHT ME.

WELL, IN THAT CASE...

...BUT IT'S A LONG TRIP. 3 DAYS TIME...YOU'LL BE ALRIGHT ON YOUR OWN?

I KNOW I'M SAFE AS LONG AS I'M HERE.

ONCE GOTHEL HAS GONE...

I KNOW WHAT YOU'RE HERE FOR AND I'M NOT AFRAID OF YOU!

WHAT?

WHO ARE YOU AND HOW DID YOU FIND ME?

OKAY, LET ME ASSURE YOU: I DON'T KNOW YOU, NOR DID I COME TO FIND YOU. BUT MAY I JUST SAY...

HI. I'M FLYNN RIDER.

WAIT! WHERE'S MY SATCHEL?

IT'S HIDDEN WHERE YOU'LL NEVER FIND IT! WHAT DO YOU WANT WITH MY HAIR?

THE ONLY THING I WANT TO DO IS GET OUT OF IT! I WAS BEING CHASED, I SAW A TOWER, I CLIMBED IT. END OF STORY.

SO...

YOU COMING, BLONDIE?

I JUST HAVE TO DO IT. SHOULD I? NO...

HERE I GO!

?

...AND THEN...

A MOMENT OF HESITATION, MERE FEET ABOVE THE GROUND...

WOO-HOO! I CAN'T BELIEVE I DID THIS!

NO. WOULD THIS BREAK HER HEART? OF COURSE!

SHE WOULD BE HEARTBROKEN. YOU'RE RIGHT.

I *AM*, AREN'T I? LET'S GO HOME, I GET BACK MY SATCHEL, YOU GET BACK YOUR MOTHER-DAUGHTER RELATIONSHIP.

NO! NO, I'M SEEING THOSE LANTERNS. AND YOU...

FRRR FRRR

AHH! WHAT IS IT? RUFFIANS? THUGS?

SORRY. I GUESS I'M A BIT JUMPY.

ARE YOU HUNGRY, BLONDIE? I KNOW A GREAT PLACE FOR LUNCH...

MEANWHILE...

SNIFF SNIFF

A PALACE HORSE? WHERE IS YOUR -- OH, NO...

...RAPUNZEL!

RAPUNZEL! LET DOWN YOUR HAIR!

BUT FOR THE FIRST TIME, NOTHING HAPPENS.

GOTHEL RUNS TO THE BACK OF THE TOWER, TO A SECRET ENTRANCE.

SNAP

SHE BURSTS THROUGH A HIDDEN DOOR IN THE FLOOR...

RAPUNZEL!

...AND ENTERS AN EMPTY TOWER. **RAPUNZEL IS GONE.**

SHE'S DESPERATE TO FIND OUT WHAT HAPPENED, SO SHE TEARS THE PLACE APART, AND FINALLY, UNDER A STAIR-STEP...

?

...THIS IS SOMETHING VERY INTERESTING!

WANTED
DEAD or ALIVE

Flynn Rider
THIEF

!

MEANWHILE...

THE SNUGGLY DUCKLING

THE SNUGGLY DUCKLING! A VERY QUAINT PLACE. PERFECT FOR YOU!

GARÇON! YOUR FINEST TABLE, PLEASE!

ARE YOU SCARED? MAYBE WE SHOULD GET YOU HOME AND CALL IT A DAY...

O-OKAY...

A PERFECT PLAN TO GET BACK THE SATCHEL, BUT...

WANTED

SLAM

IS THIS YOU?

WANTED! DEAD or ALIVE

Flynn Rider

UGH. NOW THEY'RE JUST BEING MEAN.

...THE THUGS SHOW HER A **SECRET PASSAGE!**

GO LIVE YOUR DREAM...

BUT SOMEONE IS DETERMINED TO ARREST FLYNN...

SNIFF SNIFF

A PASSAGE? COME ON, MEN!

...SOMEONE WANTS TO TAKE SOMETHING FROM HIM...

LET'S GET THE CROWN!

THACK

...AND SOMEONE ELSE WANTS HER TREASURE BACK!

WHERE DOES THAT TUNNEL LET OUT?

?!?

IN THE MEANTIME, INSIDE THE TUNNEL...

WELL, FOR THE RECORD... IT WAS GOOD OF YOU TO STEP IN. THANK YOU.

HMM... SO, FLYNN, WHERE ARE YOU FROM?

WHOA! SORRY, I DON'T DO BACKSTORY.

HOWEVER I AM VERY INTERESTED IN YOURS...

HERE'S MY QUESTION... IF YOU WANT TO SEE THE LANTERNS SO BADLY, WHY HAVEN'T YOU GONE BEFORE?

OH, WELL, I... UHH...

RIDER!

RUN! RUN, RAPUNZEL!

RAPUNZEL, FLYNN AND PASCAL FLEE THROUGH THE UNDERGROUND TUNNELS...

...BUT THEIR PURSUERS ARE EVERYWHERE!

COME ON, BLONDIE!

GRAB

SWISSH

HURRY!

TAKE MY HAIR!

WOOOH

CRACK

MAXIMUS BREAKS ONE OF THE SUPPORT BEAMS AND CATCHES UP WITH THEM...

...AND THE CAVE IS FLOODED!

RRRUMBLE

THE FLOOD CARRIES AWAY EVERYONE AND EVERYTHING...

WOOOOOOSH

CRACK

!

SPLASH

CRASH

THEY ARE TRAPPED!

OH, NO...

THUMP

THERE'S NO WAY OUT!

OUCH!

THIS IS ALL MY FAULT. SHE WAS RIGHT. I NEVER SHOULD HAVE DONE THIS. I'M SO SORRY, FLYNN.

EUGENE. MY NAME'S EUGENE FITZHERBERT. SOMEONE MIGHT AS WELL KNOW.

I HAVE MAGIC HAIR THAT GLOWS WHEN I SING.

WHAT?

AND RAPUNZEL STARTS SINGING WHILE THEY DIVE DOWN...

...AND HER HAIR GLOWS BEAUTIFULLY, LIGHTING UP THE WATER...

...REVEALING A SMALL ESCAPE HOLE IN THE CAVERN.

SPLASH

A FEW SECONDS LATER...

WE MADE IT! WE'RE ALIVE! PASCAL, WE'RE ALIVE!

THE HAIR ACTUALLY GLOWS. WHY DOES HER HAIR GLOW?

EUGENE, IT DOESN'T JUST GLOW...

?

AT THE SAME TIME, AT THE TUNNEL EXIT, GOTHEL WAITS IN VAIN FOR THEM...

THUMP

...BUT WHAT COMES OUT IS A USEFUL SURPRISE!

WE'LL KILL THAT RIDER! AND GET BACK THE CROWN!

OR PERHAPS YOU WANT TO STOP AND THINK FOR A MOMENT?

I COULD OFFER YOU SOMETHING WORTH MORE THAN A CROWN... AND IT COMES WITH REVENGE ON FLYNN RIDER.

LATER, IN THE WOODS...

♪♪♪

BUT...YOUR HAIR...HOW DID IT--

I DON'T KNOW. PEOPLE TRIED TO TAKE IT ONCE, BUT WHEN IT'S CUT IT LOSES ITS POWER. THAT'S WH' MOTHER NEVER LET ME...I'VE NEVER...

YOU'VE NEVER LEFT THE TOWER.

SO, EUGENE FITZHERBERT, HUH?

THERE WAS THIS BOOK WHEN I WAS YOUNG. *THE TALES OF FLYNNIGAN RIDER!*

HE HAD ENOUGH MONEY TO DO ANYTHING, TO GO ANYWHERE! FOR A KID WITH NOTHING... HE WAS A HERO. **MY HERO.**

FOR THE RECORD...I LIKE EUGENE FITZHERBERT MUCH MORE THAN FLYNN RIDER...

WELL, I...I SHOULD GET SOME MORE FIREWOOD...

BUT ONCE FLYNN'S GONE...

FINALLY! I THOUGHT HE'D NEVER LEAVE.

FRUSH

GASP! MOTHER! HOW...HOW DID YOU FIND ME?

IT WAS EASY. I JUST FOLLOWED THE SOUND OF COMPLETE AND UTTER BETRAYAL!

WE'RE GOING HOME, RAPUNZEL. NOW!

YOU DON'T UNDERSTAND. I'VE MET SOMEONE. HE...

...HE LIKES ME.

LIKES YOU? PLEASE, RAPUNZEL! THIS IS WHY HE'S HERE, THE ONLY REASON.

GIVE IT TO HIM! GO AND TEST HIM...AND YOU'LL SEE.

WILL SHE HAVE THE COURAGE TO TEST EUGENE?

FOR NOW, RAPUNZEL HAS NO ANSWER. FOR NOW, SHE WILL HIDE THE SATCHEL.

THE NEXT MORNING, FLYNN AND RAPUNZEL WAKE UP WITH A BAD SURPRISE...

PLEASE, KNOW THAT I'M OPPOSED TO VIOLENCE!

HEY! EASY, EASY, BOY...

SWIP

YOU'RE A GOOD BOY. AREN'T YOU TIRED FROM CHASING THIS BAD MAN ALL OVER THE PLACE?

LOOK, TODAY IS KIND OF THE **BIGGEST DAY** OF MY LIFE AND...

...I NEED YOU NOT TO GET HIM ARRESTED. JUST FOR 24 HOURS, OKAY?

IT'S ALSO MY BIRTHDAY, JUST SO YOU KNOW...

DING-DONG-DING-DONG

BELLS?

!

AND THERE IT IS. RAPUNZEL, FOR THE FIRST TIME, SEES THE **KINGDOM**.

LATER, A PERFECT DAY BEGINS...

KINGDOM FLAGS!

THANK YOU!

...A DAY OF CELEBRATION IN THE KINGDOM...

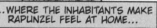

...WHERE THE INHABITANTS MAKE RAPUNZEL FEEL AT HOME...

...SHE EXPERIENCES MYSTERIOUS EMOTIONS...

...AND DANCES TO HER HEART'S DELIGHT!

AND WHEN THE SUN GOES DOWN, AND THE MOMENT IS COMING...

WHAT IF IT'S NOT EVERYTHING I DREAMED IT WOULD BE, EUGENE? AND WHAT IF IT IS? WHAT DO I DO THEN?

THAT'S THE GOOD PART, I GUESS...

YOU GET TO FIND A NEW DREAM.

!?

...SUDDENLY THE NIGHT SKY IS FILLED WITH FLYING LANTERNS...

...IT'S ALL RAPUNZEL'S BEEN WAITING FOR...

...HER DREAM COME TRUE.

EVERYTHING SEEMS PERFECT.

I HAVE SOMETHING FOR YOU, TOO. I SHOULD HAVE GIVEN IT TO YOU BEFORE, BUT I WAS SCARED. AND THE THING IS...

...I'M NOT SCARED ANYMORE. YOU KNOW WHAT I MEAN?

YEAH. YEAH, I DO.

FLYNN SETS THE SATCHEL TO THE SIDE. HE COULD CARE LESS...

BUT, ALL OF A SUDDEN, EVERYTHING GOES WRONG.

THE STABBINGTON BROTHERS!

I'M SORRY, THERE'S SOMETHING I HAVE TO TAKE CARE OF...

IT'S ALRIGHT, PASCAL.

THE CROWN IS ALL YOURS. I'LL MISS IT, BUT I THINK IT'S FOR THE BEST.

THERE.

TINK

WE HEARD YOU FOUND SOMETHING MUCH MORE VALUABLE THAN A CROWN, RIDER.

WE WANT HER, INSTEAD.

!

OH, EUGENE! I WAS STARTING TO THINK YOU RAN OFF WITH THE CROWN AND LEFT ME...

HE DID.

WHAT? NO, HE WOULDN'T!

SEE FOR YOURSELF. A **FAIR TRADE**: A CROWN FOR THE GIRL WITH THE MAGIC HAIR...

NO... NO, PLEASE! NO!

TAKE HER!

THIS WAY!

THUMP THUMP CRASH

?

OH, MY PRECIOUS GIRL!

MOTHER?!

I WAS SO WORRIED, SO I FOLLOWED YOU AND I SAW THEM ATTACK YOU AND... ARE YOU ALRIGHT? ARE YOU HURT?

YOU WERE RIGHT, MOTHER. YOU WERE RIGHT ABOUT EVERYTHING...

I KNOW, DARLING. I KNOW.

LOOK! THE CROWN!

UH? WHAT? RAPUNZEL? RAPUNZEL?

EVERYTHING IS WRONG. AND MAXIMUS IS THE ONLY ONE WHO CAN DO SOMETHING.

LATER, AT THE KINGDOM PRISON...

LET'S GET THIS OVER WITH, RIDER.

YOU?!

HOW DID YOU KNOW ABOUT HER? TELL ME, NOW!

IT WASN'T US. IT WAS THE OLD LADY.

OLD LADY?

WAIT! YOU DON'T UNDERSTAND, SHE'S IN TROUBLE!

THE GUARDS LEAD HIM AWAY...

...WHEN SUDDENLY ALL THE DOORS SHUT, TRAPPING THEM!

BAM

WHAT'S THIS?

OPEN UP!

PASSWORD?

WHAT?

NOPE.

THE TAVERN GUYS! MAXIMUS TOOK THEM TO SAVE FLYNN AND TAKE HIM TO RAPUNZEL'S TOWER...

...WHERE EVERYTHING IS JUST AS IF NOTHING EVER HAPPENED.

BLUE? OH, COME ON. IT'S NOT THAT BAD.

OR IS IT? RAPUNZEL HOLDS THE FLAG FROM HER DAY IN THE KINGDOM AND LOOKS AT THE CEILING...

SHE LOOKS AT THE FLAG, THEN BACK TO HER PAINTINGS. SUDDENLY, THE DRAWINGS DISAPPEAR, LEAVING ONLY THE SYMBOL OF THE KINGDOM!

AND SHE UNDERSTANDS.

SHE REMEMBERS EVERYTHING -- THE KING, THE QUEEN, THE CROWN, THE LOST PRINCESS...

FREEDOM! WITH THE HELP OF HIS NEW FRIENDS, FLYNN RIDES MAXIMUS TO RAPUNZEL'S TOWER...

RAPUNZEL, LET DOWN YOUR HAIR!

...THE HAIR FLOWS TO THE GROUND AND HE CLIMBS IT...

...SUSPECTING NOTHING...

I THOUGHT I'D NEVER SEE YOU AGAIN.

MMPF!

...BUT IT'S TOO LATE!

DON'T WORRY, HANDSOME...

STAB

NO! -MMMPFT- LET ME SAVE HIM!

AND WHY WOULD I DO THAT, DEAR?

IF YOU LET ME SAVE HIM, I'LL NEVER TRY TO ESCAPE...JUST LET ME HEAL HIM AND YOU AND I WILL BE TOGETHER FOREVER JUST LIKE YOU WANT.

PROMISE!

I, T PROMISE. JUST LET ME HEAL HIM.

EUGENE!

EUGENE! OH NO...I'M SO SORRY. BUT I'LL DO IT, NO MATTER WHAT I'LL SAVE YOU...

NO, DON'T DO THIS.

I'LL BE FINE...IF YOU ARE OK, I'LL BE FINE.

RAPUNZEL, WAIT...

ZACK

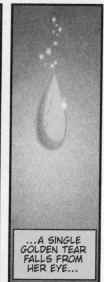
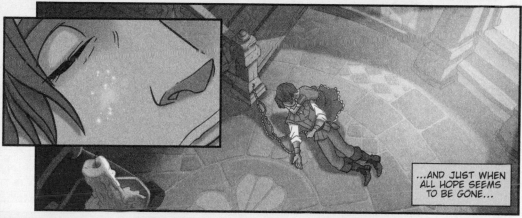

"FINALLY, RAPUNZEL RETURNED HOME. THE FAMILY WAS REUNITED."

"THE KINGDOM REJOICED FOR THEIR LOST PRINCESS HAD COME BACK."

"AND SO, ESPECIALLY FOR THE TWO OF US..."

"...DREAMS CAME TRUE ALL OVER THE PLACE."

The End

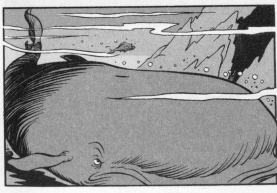

AND *NOW*, FOLKS, GRACING TONIGHT'S CONCERT WITH HIS AUGUST PRESENCE--

--HIS ROYAL HIGHNESS--

--KING TRITON!

HOORAY! LONG LIVE THE KING!!

TRA-TRA-TERRAH!

NEXT, PRESENTING THE DISTINGUISHED COURT *COMPOSER*--

--HORATIO FELONIOUS IGNACIOUS CRUSTACEOUS *SEBASTIAN!*

I'M REALLY LOOKING *FORWARD* TO THIS PER-FORMANCE, SEBASTIAN! I KNOW YOU WON'T LET ME *DOWN!!*

AH, YOUR MAJESTY--

--YOUR DAUGHTERS' DAY WILL BE *SPECTACU-LAR!*

YES, AND ESPECIALLY MY LITTLE *ARIEL!*

UMM--YES, SHE HAS THE *MOST* BEAUTIFUL VOICE OF *ALL!*

IF ONLY SHE WOULD SHOW UP FOR *REHEARSAL* ONCE IN A WHILE!

♪ THE DAUGHTERS OF TRITON ARE WE... OUR FATHER HAS CHOSEN EACH NAME FOR US WELL-- ♪

♪ --LISTEN NOW TO OUR SISTER WHOSE VOICE RINGS LIKE A *BELL!* ♪

♪ HER NAME IS ARIE-- ♪

≡GASP!≡

OH, NO!

ARIEL!!

HAVE YOU *EVER* SEEN ANYTHING SO *WONDERFUL* IN YOUR *ENTIRE* LIFE?

IT'S *COOL!*

BUT--UH-- WHAT *IS* IT?

HOW DO *I* KNOW?

BUT I BET *SCUTTLE* DOES!

I WONDER WHAT *THIS* ONE IS...

ARIEL!

HELP! SHARK!!

CRASH!

HURRY, FLOUNDER!

HEY! WHAT'RE YA *DOIN'?*

THROCK!

≡WHEW!≡

WHOA! IT'S ARIEL! HO! MUST BE A MILE OFF THE PORT BOW!

I GOTTA *GO!* THANK YOU, SCUTTLE!

ANYTIME, SWEETIE! *ANYTIME!*

LOOK! KING TRITON'S *YOUNGEST!*

YEAH!

URSULA WILL BE VERY INTERESSSSTED!

AHAAAA!!

YES, HURRY HOME, PRINCESS! WE WOULDN'T WANT TO MISS OLD DADDY'S *CELEBRATION*--NOW *WOULD* WE!?

HMPH! CELEBRA-TION *INDEED!*

WE HAD FANTASTICAL FEASTS WHEN *I* LIVED IN THE PALACE! AND LOOK AT ME *NOW*--WASTED AWAY TO PRACTICALLY *NOTHING!*

BANISHED AND *EXILED* BY TRITON AND ≡MUNCH!≡ PRACTICALLY *STARVING* WHILE HE AND HIS FISH FOLK *CELEBRATE!*

WELL, I'LL GIVE 'EM SOMETHING TO CELEBRATE SOON *ENOUGH!*

FLOTSAM! JETSAM!

I WANT YOU TO KEEP AN EXTRA CLOSE *WATCH* ON TRITON'S PRETTY, LITTLE *DAUGHTER!*

I HAVE A HUNCH *SHE MAY BE THE KEY* TO HIS *UNDOING!* HEE-HEE-HEEE!

I JUST DON'T KNOW WHAT WE'RE GOING TO *DO* WITH YOU, YOUNG LADY! AS A RESULT OF YOUR *CARELESS BEHAVIOR--*

--CARELESS AND RECKLESS BEHAVIOR--

--THE CONCERT WAS--

WELL, IT WAS COMPLETELY *DESTROYED,* DAT'S ALL!

HEY!

IT WASN'T *HER* FAULT!

THIS *SHARK* CHASED US... GRR!...AND... AND...WE... *WHOA!*

...AND THEN THIS SEAGULL CAME AND IT WAS, "THIS IS THIS, AND THAT IS..."

SEA-GULL!?!

YOU WENT UP TO THE *SURFACE* AGAIN, DIDN'T YOU? *DIDN'T* YOU?

ARIEL, *HOW MANY TIMES* MUST WE GO *THROUGH* THIS?! YOU COULD HAVE BEEN *SEEN* BY THOSE BARBARIANS-- THOSE *HUMANS!*

DADDY, THEY'RE *NOT* BARBARIANS, AND I'M SIXTEEN YEARS OLD!

I'M *NOT* A CHILD ANY MORE!

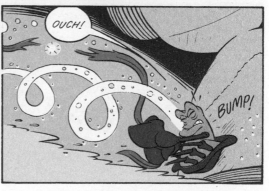

OH, I SEE--YOUR COLLECTION! IF YOUR FATHER KNEW ABOUT DIS--

YOU'RE NOT GONNA TELL HIM, ARE YOU?

COME WID ME! I'LL TAKE YOU HOME, AND--

OH, PLEASE, SEBASTIAN! DADDY WOULD NEVER UNDERSTAND!

LOOK!

ARIEL! COME BACK HERE!

OOOOH!

POP!

BANG!

WHIZZZ

=GASP!= JUMPIN' JELLYFISH!!

OH, SHE'S OUT THERE *SOME-WHERE!* I JUST--HAVEN'T *FOUND* HER YET!

PERHAPS YOU HAVEN'T BEEN *LOOKING* HARD ENOUGH!

HA! BELIEVE *ME,* GRIM, WHEN I FIND HER I'LL *KNOW!*

IT'LL JUST--*BAM!*--HIT ME LIKE LIGHTNING!

ZAP!

ZIP!

WHOOOSH!

STORM COMING UP!

ZAP!

SECURE THE RIGGING!

ZZZZAP!

HEAVE-HO!!

THE HELM!

SWASHHH!

ARGH!

KING TRITON'S HEADSTRONG, LOVESICK GIRL WOULD MAKE SUCH A CHARMING ADDITION TO MY LITTLE GARDEN!

ELSEWHERE...

I'VE GOT TO SEE HIM AGAIN! SCUTTLE KNOWS WHERE HE LIVES!

ARIEL, PLEASE!

LIFE UNDER DA SEA IS BETTER THAN ANYTHING THEY GOT UP DERE!

LOOK AT DA WORLD AROUND YOU RIGHT HERE ON DA OCEAN FLOOR!

SUCH WONDERFUL TINGS SURROUND YOU! WHAT MORE IS YOU LOOKING FOR?

UP ON DA SHORE, DEY WORK ALL DAY...WHILE WE DEVOTIN' FULL TIME TO FLOATIN'!

DAT'S WHY IT'S BETTER DOWN WHERE IT'S WETTER... UNDA DA SEA!

WHY CAN'T YOU JUST TELL ME WHAT THIS IS ALL ABOUT?

YOU'LL SEE! IT'S--

--A SURPRISE!

OH, FLOUNDER, YOU'RE THE BEST!

IT LOOKS JUST LIKE HIM!

WHY, ERIC--RUN AWAY WITH YOU? THIS IS ALL SO--SO SUDDEN!

HE'S QUITE A *CATCH*, ISN'T HE? WELL, ANGEL-FISH, THE SOLUTION TO YOUR PROBLEM IS *SIMPLE*--

--THE ONLY WAY TO GET WHAT YOU *WANT* IS TO BECOME A HUMAN *YOURSELF!*

=GASP!= CAN YOU *DO* THAT?

MY DEAR SWEET CHILD, IT'S WHAT I *LIVE* FOR--TO HELP UNFORTUNATE MERFOLK LIKE *YOURSELF!*

SNAP! SNAP!

ONE GIRL WISHES SHE WERE *SKINNY*, ONE BOY WANTS A GIRL OF HIS *OWN!* CAN I *HELP* THEM? WELL, OF *COURSE!*

NATURALLY, THERE'S A *FEE*--AND THAT'S WHAT *HAPPENS* IF ONE DOESN'T *PAY!* ONE IS CHANGED INTO A *POLYP!*

NOW HERE'S THE *DEAL:* I'LL TURN YOU INTO A HUMAN FOR THREE DAYS--GOT THAT? *THREE* DAYS!

NOW THIS IS *IMPORTANT:* BEFORE THE SUN SETS ON THE THIRD DAY, YOU'VE GOT TO GET DEAR, OLD PRINCIE TO *KISS* YOU!

NOT JUST *ANY* KISS! A *SPECIAL* KISS--THE KISS OF *TRUE LOVE!* AND YOU'LL REMAIN HUMAN *PERMANENTLY*--

--BUT IF HE *DOESN'T* KISS YOU YOU'LL TURN BACK INTO A *MERMAID*--

--AND *THEN* YOU BELONG TO *ME!*

NO, ARIEL!

DON'T!

IF I BECOME *HUMAN,* I'LL NEVER BE WITH MY *FATHER* OR *SISTERS* AGAIN!

BUT YOU'LL HAVE YOUR *MAN!* LIFE'S *FULL* OF TOUGH CHOICES, ISN'T IT?!

BUT I ALMOST *FORGOT* THE SUBJECT OF *PAYMENT!*

ALL I WANT FROM *YOU,* MY DEAR, IS--

--YOUR *VOICE!*

M-MY *VOICE?*

BUT WITHOUT MY *VOICE,* HOW CAN I--?

SPEAK WITH YOUR *EYES,* YOUR LOVELY *SMILE!* BESIDES, MEN THERE DON'T LIKE A LOT OF *CHATTER!*

MAKE UP YOUR *MIND!* I HAVE NO TIME TO *WASTE!*

UH--

Sign Here

OH, *NO!!*

LIFT, FLOUNDER! LIFT!

FASTER!

MEAN-WHILE...

THAT GIRL'S VOICE! I CAN'T GET IT OUT OF MY MIND!

I'VE LOOKED EVERYWHERE, MAX! WHERE COULD SHE BE?

ARIEL!

LOOK AT YA! THERE'S SUMPIN' DIFFERENT!

SHE'S GOT LEGS, YOU IDIOT! SHE TRADED HER VOICE TO DA SEA WITCH!

SHE'S GOTTA MAKE THE PRINCE FALL IN LOVE AND KISS HER-- IN ONLY THREE DAYS!

WAIT! I KNOW JUST THE THING SHE NEEDS!

MAX! WHAT'S GOTTEN INTO YOU, FELLA?

WOOF! WOOF!

YAH LOOK SENSATIONAL NOW, KID, TANKS TO ME AND THAT OL' SAIL CLOTH!

WOOF! WOOF!

OH!

SORRY IF THIS KNUCKLE-HEAD *SCARED* YOU... HE'S *HARMLESS*, REALLY!

ER...YOU SEEM *VERY FAMILIAR* TO ME! HAVE WE *MET*?

YOU CAN'T *SPEAK*!

=SIGH!= THEN YOU *COULDN'T* BE WHO I *THOUGHT*!

WHOA! CAREFUL!

GEE, YOU MUST'VE REALLY BEEN THROUGH *SOMETHING*! DON'T WORRY--

--*I'LL* HELP YOU! COME ON, YOU'LL BE OKAY!

SOON...

WASHED UP FROM A SHIP-WRECK! YOU POOR *DEAR*!

WELL, WE'LL HAVE YOU IN CLEAN CLOTHES AND FEELING BETTER IN *NO* TIME!

THE THIRD MORNING...

ARIEL! WAKE UP! CONGRATU-LATIONS!

WE *DID* IT, KIDDO!

THE WHOLE *TOWN'S* BUZZING ABOUT THE PRINCE GETTING HIMSELF *HITCHED* THIS AFTERNOON!

JUST WANNA WISH YOU *LUCK!* SEE YOU AT THE WEDDING-- I WOULDN'T *MISS* IT!

WHAT IS DIS IDIOT *BABBLING* ABOUT??

NOW, ERIC--ER--IT APPEARS I WAS *MISTAKEN!* THIS--UM--MYSTERY MAIDEN OF YOURS *DOES* IN FACT *EXIST!*

AND SHE IS *LOVELY!* CON-GRATU...

WE WISH TO BE MARRIED AS SOON AS *POSSIBLE!*

OF *COURSE*, ERIC, BUT THESE THINGS DO TAKE TIME, AND--

THIS AFTER-NOON, GRIMSBY!

THE WEDDING SHIP DEPARTS BEFORE *SUNSET!*

≡SIGH!≡ AS YOU *WISH*, ERIC!

THE SUN HAS *SET!!*

HAHAHAHA HAHAHAAA!

HAHAHAHA HAHAAAH!

SO LONG-- LOVER-BOY!

POOR LITTLE PRINCESS, IT'S NOT *YOU* I'M AFTER! I'VE A MUCH *BIGGER* FISH TO FRY!

WHY, KING TRITON--HAHAHA! HOW *ARE* YOU?

LET HER GO!

NOT A *CHANCE!* SHE AND I MADE A *DEAL!*

DADDY, I'M SORRY!

HERE IS WHAT I THINK OF YOUR *DEAL!*

ZZAP!

THIS CONTRACT'S LEGAL, BINDING AND COMPLETELY *UNBREAKABLE*-- EVEN FOR *YOU*!

OF COURSE, THE DAUGHTER OF THE GREAT *SEA KING* IS A VERY PRECIOUS COMMODITY--BUT I MIGHT BE WILLING TO MAKE AN *EXCHANGE* FOR SOMEONE EVEN *BETTER*!

ERIC, WHAT ARE YOU *DOING*?

GRIM, I LOST HER *ONCE*, I'M NOT GOING TO LOSE HER *AGAIN*!

NOW, DO WE HAVE A DEAL?

HA! IT'S *DONE*, THEN!

TRITON

HAHAHAHAAAAA!

NO! OH, NO!

SOMETHING'S *HAPPENING* DOWN THERE!

DADDY ?!?

OH, YOUR *MAJES-TY*!

AT *LAST*, THE CROWN IS *MINE*!

HA-HA-HAAAA!

WHEN THERE'S WORK TO DONE, IT'S SHARE AND SHARE ALIKE.

HARMPH! AM I GOOD OR *WHAT*?

BUT MOMENTS LATER...

HEY, WHO'S THE *WISE GUY*?!

Aladdin

HOP ON, PRINCESS! TIME FOR A *SUPER-EXOTIC* CARPET TRIP!

SUPER-EXOTIC? NEAT! WHERE *TO?*

THE *PYRAMIDS* OF *GIZA!* A RARE SIGHT THAT FEW IN AGRABAH HAVE SEEN!

OOH! I'VE *ALWAYS WANTED* TO SEE GIZA!

MY COUSIN SHARMA SAW GIZA ON HER HONEYMOON. UNCLE ZAHBIR WENT THERE LAST YEAR, *TOO.*

OH?

MY EIGHTH COUSIN SCHEHERAZADE *TALKS* AND *TALKS* ABOUT IT. AND AUNT MASIRA—

⸮HMM!⸮ SUDDENLY GIZA DOESN'T SEEM SO *EXOTIC* ANYMORE.

HEY... I *TRIED.*

GENIE TOLD ME NOBODY WENT THERE, OKAY?

GENIE SPENT TOO LONG IN A *LAMP.*

GIZA MALL
EXIT 29

End

NEW ORLEANS, ABOUT A HUNDRED YEARS AGO.

THE EVENING STAR IS SHINING BRIGHT, AND ANYTHING CAN HAPPEN...

"OH, PLEASE, DEAR PRINCESS," SAID THE FROG. "ONLY A KISS FROM YOU CAN BREAK THIS TERRIBLE SPELL INFLICTED ON ME BY A WICKED WITCH!"

AND THE PRINCESS KISSED THAT LITTLE FROG! THEN, THE FROG WAS TRANSFORMED INTO A **HANDSOME PRINCE!**

OH, READ IT AGAIN!

!

SORRY, **CHARLOTTE!** IT'S TIME FOR US TO GO...

I'LL NEVER KISS A FROG! YUCK!

I WOULD DO IT, **TIANA**, IF I COULD MARRY A PRINCE AND BE A PRINCESS!

EVENING, EUDORA...

DADDY?

DADDY! LOOK AT MY NEW DRESS... ISN'T IT PRETTY?

WHY, I'D EXPECT NOTHING LESS FROM EUDORA, THE FINEST SEAMSTRESS IN NEW ORLEANS!

COME ALONG, TIANA...

TIANA'S HOME IS IN THE 9TH WARD, A COZY PLACE FULL OF WARMTH, CHARM AND CHARACTER.

THERE SHE LEARNS HOW TO COOK WITH HER FATHER, WHO TEACHES HER THAT FOOD HELPS BRING FAMILY AND FRIENDS TOGETHER.

THEY DREAM OF ONE DAY OWNING **THEIR** OWN MARVELOUS **RESTAURANT.**

MMM... THIS IS THE BEST GUMBO I'VE EVER TASTED, TIANA!

EUDORA, OUR LITTLE GIRL HAS A GIFT!

LATER...

WHEN I OPEN UP MY OWN RESTAURANT, PEOPLE ARE GONNA LINE UP TO GET A TASTE OF MY FOOD!

OUR FOOD!

THAT'S RIGHT, BABY... **OUR** FOOD!

DADDY, LOOK! IF YOU MAKE A WISH ON THE EVENING STAR, IT'S SURE TO COME TRUE...

YES, BUT YOU'VE GOT TO HELP IT ALONG WITH SOME **HARD WORK** OF YOUR OWN!

YOU KNOW, SO I CAN...

SO YOU CAN SAVE MONEY FOR YOUR RESTAURANT, I KNOW, I KNOW!

DLING

OH, GOOD MORNING, **MR. LABOUFF**...CONGRATULATIONS ON BEING VOTED **KING** OF THE MARDI GRAS PARADE!

THANKS...WOW, BEIGNETS!

TIANA! DID YOU HEAR THE NEWS? **PRINCE NAVEEN** IS COMING TO NEW ORLEANS!

YES! AND HE'S STAYING--

HE'S STAYING AT OUR HOUSE AS MY PERSONAL GUEST!

OH, **CHARLOTTE**, THAT'S SWELL!

EXCUSE ME DADDY. TIANA, I NEED ABOUT 500 OF YOUR SPECIAL BEIGNETS FOR MY BALL!

WILL THIS ABOUT COVER IT?

THAT'S IT! I'M GETTING MY OWN RESTAURANT!

TONIGHT MY PRINCE IS COMING...AND I SURE WON'T LET HIM GO!

THAT AFTERNOON, TIANA GOES TO BUY HER RESTAURANT!

EVERYTHING LOOKS PEACHY KEEN, MR. FENNER...

FENNER BROS. REALTY

FOR SALE

WE'LL HAVE ALL THE PAPERS READY TO SIGN AFTER MARDI GRAS!

WHY DON'T I SIGN THEM TONIGHT, WHEN I SEE YOU AT THE LABOUFFS' MASQUERADE BALL?

FENNER BROS. REALTY OR SALE

YOU DRIVE A HARD BARGAIN, TIANA!

TABLE FOR ONE, PLEASE! I BROUGHT A LITTLE SOMETHING TO GET YOU STARTED.

MAMA-- DADDY'S GUMBO POT!

I KNOW. I MISS HIM, TOO.

NOW, LET'S GO TAKE A LOOK.

OH, LOOK AT IT! DOESN'T IT JUST MAKE YOU WANT TO CRY?

YEEESSS...

GENTLEMEN, ENCHANTÉ'! A TIP OF THE HAT FROM **DR. FACILIER!**

"TAROT READINGS, CHARMS, POTIONS, DREAMS MADE REAL..." **ACHIDANZA!**

WERE I A BETTING MAN--AND I'M NOT--I'D WAGER I'M IN THE COMPANY OF VISITING ROYALTY!

SIRE!

LAWRENCE, THIS GENTLEMAN HAS JUST READ MY PALM!

...OR THIS MORNING'S NEWSPAPER! SIRE, THIS CHAP IS A CHARLATAN!

BUT THE CHARMING FACILIER CONVINCES THEM TO ENTER HIS **TAROT CARD SHOP...**

SIT DOWN AND RELAX!

YOUR LIFESTYLE'S HIGH, BUT YOUR FUNDS ARE LOW...YOU NEED TO MARRY A LITTLE HONEY WHOSE DADDY'S GOT DOUGH!

YOU JUST WANT TO BE FREE, BUT FREEDOM TAKES *GREEN!*

?

IT'S THE *GREEN* YOU NEED AND, INTO YOUR FUTURE, IT'S THE *GREEN* I SEE!

YOU? YOU'VE BEEN PUSHED AROUND ALL YOUR LIFE!

BUT IN YOUR FUTURE, THE YOU I SEE, IS THE MAN YOU ALWAYS WANTED TO BE!

!

SHAKE MY HAND! ARE YOU READY? *TRANSFORMATION CENTRAL!*

FACILIER GRABS A TALISMAN...

TRANSMOGRIFICATION!

OUCH!

THE MAGICAL TALISMAN BITES NAVEEN'S FINGER...

CAN YOU FEEL IT? YOU'RE CHANGING! **CHANGING!**

...AND ABSORBS HIS **BLOOD**, WHILE SOMETHING IS HAPPENING TO NAVEEN AND LAWRENCE!

BLAME MY FRIENDS ON THE OTHER SIDE...

YOU GOT WHAT YOU WANTED BUT YOU LOST WHAT YOU HAD!

HA, HA, HA!

THAT EVENING, AT THE LABOUFF ESTATE...

LADIES AND GENTLEMEN, HIS ROYAL HIGHNESS, PRINCE NAVEEN!

CHARLOTTE RACES DOWN THE STAIRS AND STARTS DANCING WITH THE PRINCE.

WOW!

MARVELOUS PARTY!

OH! GOOD EVENING, MR. FENNER AND...MR. FENNER!

FINE SMELLING BEIGNETS!

ONCE I SIGN THOSE PAPERS YOU'VE BROUGHT, THEY'LL BE THE HOUSE SPECIALTY!

YES, ABOUT THAT...

YOU WERE OUTBID!

A FELLOW CAME IN OFFERING THE FULL AMOUNT IN CASH! UNLESS YOU CAN TOP HIS OFFER BY WEDNESDAY...

...YOU CAN KISS THAT PLACE GOODBYE!

WHAT? WAIT A MINUTE!

CRASH

STOCK

POOR TIANA! WHAT IS SHE GOING TO DO NOW?

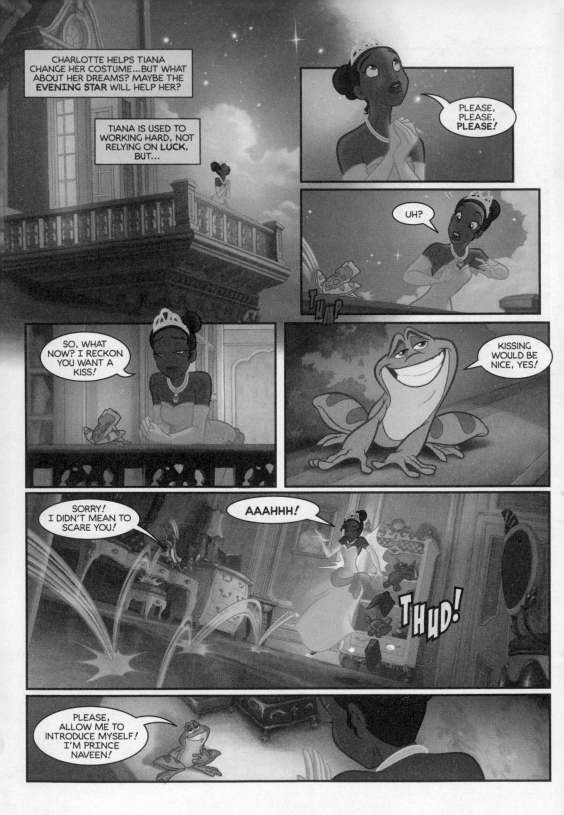

HOLD ON, IF YOU ARE THE PRINCE, THEN WHO WAS WALTZING WITH CHARLOTTE ON THE DANCE FLOOR?

ALL I KNOW IS ONE MINUTE I AM A PRINCE...

...AND NEXT I AM TRIPPING OVER THESE!

HMM...

WAIT! I KNOW THIS STORY!

"THE FROG PRINCE?"

YES! AND THIS IS EXACTLY THE ANSWER...

...YOU MUST KISS ME!

LOOK, I'D REALLY LIKE TO HELP YOU, BUT I JUST DO NOT KISS FROGS!

OH, BUT YOU MUST!

I COME FROM A WEALTHY FAMILY! SURELY YOU HAVE A WISH I COULD GRANT...

171

IN THE MEANTIME, FACILIER ALREADY KNOWS WHAT'S HAPPENED!

YOU LET THE PRINCE GO?

YES...

I CAN'T GO THROUGH WITH THIS!

POP POP

POOF

YOU WEAR THIS GHASTLY THING!

CAREFUL WITH THAT!

GRAB

FUN FACT ABOUT MAGIC, LARRY... I CAN'T CONJURE A THING FOR MYSELF!

BAD MAGIC? THIS ALL HAPPENED BECAUSE YOU WERE MESSING WITH **DR. FACILIER?**

HE WAS VERY CHARISMATIC!

THE ONLY WAY TO GET WHAT YOU WANT IS THROUGH **HARD WORK!**

HARD WORK?

WHY WOULD A PRINCESS NEED TO WORK HARD?

I'M NOT A PRINCESS! I'M A WAITRESS!

A WAITRESS?! NO WONDER THE KISS DIDN'T WORK! YOU LIED TO ME!

I NEVER SAID I WAS A **PRINCESS!**

BUT YOU... YOU WERE WEARING A CROWN!

IT WAS A COSTUME PARTY!

OH, YEAH? WELL, BY THE WAY, I AM COMPLETELY **BROKE!** HA HA! HA...

AAAAAH!

POP!

POP

POP

!

SPLASH!!

YOU'RE BROKE! AND YOU HAD THE GALL TO CALL ME A LIAR?

AAHH! RUN!

I :PUFF: INTEND TO BE RICH AGAIN ONCE I MARRY CHARLOTTE LABOUFF--IF SHE'LL HAVE ME!

ARE YOU REALLY A PRINCE?

OBVIOUSLY!

THEN SHE'LL HAVE YOU!

THUD

PUNK

ALL RIGHT...I KNOW CHARLOTTE WILL BE HAPPY. AND ONCE YOU TWO ARE MARRIED, YOU'RE GOING TO KEEP YOUR PROMISE AND GET ME MY RESTAURANT!

A LITTLE MUSIC TO PADDLE BY?

I COULD USE A LITTLE **HELP!**

?

HEY! I KNOW THAT TUNE!

TA-TA-TAT-TA

OH!

NICE TO MEET YOU, MY NAME IS **LOUIS!**

WHERE DID YOU LEARN TO PLAY LIKE THAT?

THE BAYOU IS THE BEST JAZZ SCHOOL! ALL THE GREATS PLAY THE **RIVERBOATS.** I TRIED ONCE, BUT I SCARED EVERYONE...

AND YOU? WHERE ARE **YOU** GOING?

TO FIND SOMEBODY TO BREAK THIS **SPELL!**

WE'RE NOT FROGS! WE'RE **HUMANS!**

HE GOT HIMSELF TURNED INTO A FROG BY A SHADOWY VILLAIN'S MAGIC AND I--

MAGIC? LIKE THE KIND **MAMA ODIE** DOES?

SHE'S GOT ALL KINDS OF SPELLS!

COULD YOU TAKE US TO HER?

THROUGH THE DEEPEST DEEPEST **DARKEST** PART OF THE BAYOU? **NO!**

LOUIS...

IF ONLY YOU WERE SMALLER AND LESS TOOTHY, YOU COULD PLAY JAZZ TO ADORING CROWDS WITHOUT **SCARING** THEM!

HEY! WHAT IF I ASK MAMA ODIE TO TURN ME HUMAN?

LOUIS, YOU ARE A GENIUS!

MEANWHILE LAWRENCE, THE **FAKE NAVEEN**, IS COURTING CHARLOTTE, **BUT...**

DEAR MISS CHARLOTTE, I...

SPROING

BUT... WHAT'S HAPPENING TO YOUR **EAR?!**

WHAT?

OH! THOSE **MOSQUITOS**...

THE TALISMAN IS RUNNING OUT OF **MAGIC!** LAWRENCE HAS TO **HURRY UP!**

BOING!

ERR...WOULD YOU DO ME THE HONOR OF BECOMING...

...PRINCESS OF MALDONIA?

YES! I WILL MARRY YOU!

OH, THERE IS SO MUCH TO PLAN! THE GUEST LIST! THE DRESS...

!

W-WHAT DO WE DO NOW?

BECAUSE YOU LET OUR FROGGY PRINCE GO...

...I HAVE TO ASK FOR HELP FROM MY FRIENDS ON THE **OTHER SIDE!**

IN FACT, BACK IN FACILIER'S SHOP...

FRIENDS!

I'LL SOON HAVE THE ENTIRE CITY...

...IN THE PALM OF MY HAND!

AND YOU'LL HAVE ALL THE WAYWARD SOULS YOUR DARK LITTLE HEARTS DESIRE!

RUUUMBLE

BUT WE NEED TO FIND OURSELVES A FROG! SEARCH EVERYWHERE!

"AND BRING HIM TO ME, ALIVE!"

IN THE MEANTIME, TIANA AND NAVEEN GOT HUNGRY. BUT, BY TRYING TO CATCH THE SAME BUG, THEY GOT STUCK IN A...**TIGHT** SITUATION...

WHY DID YOU TRY TO CATCH THAT INSECT?

WHY DID **YOU**? NOW WE'RE STUCK TOGETHER!

HEE-HEE! I THINK I MAY BE OF SOME HELP...

HANG ON... I'M JUST GOING TO GIVE A LITTLE TWIST HERE...

S N A P!

MY NAME IS RAYMOND, BUT EVERYBODY CALLS ME **RAY!**

YOU MUST BE NEW AROUND HERE, HUH?

ACTUALLY...

SPLASH

WE WERE ON OUR WAY TO MAMA ODIE'S, BECAUSE WE--

WHOA, WHOA! YOU'RE HEADED THE WRONG **DIRECTIONAL!**

...HEM...I WAS CONFUSED BY THE GEOGRAPHY, THE C-CHOREOGRAPHY...

WELL, ME AND MY RELATIONALS WILL HELP SHOW YOU THE WAY!

THE FIREFLIES LIGHT THE WAY THROUGH THE BAYOU...

COULD SOMETHING BE GROWING BETWEEN TIANA AND NAVEEN?

LOVE ALWAYS FINDS A WAY, IT'S TRUE... AND I LOVE YOUUU...

MAYBE...

WE... UM...

WE'D BETTER GET MOVING...

BUT...

!

GRAB

OH, NO!

NAVEEN!

AAAHHH! HELP ME!

185

AND YOU... YOUR DADDY WAS A LOVING MAN! WHAT HE HAD IN **HIM**...

...YOU'VE GOT **IN YOU!** BUT YOU'VE GOT TO DIG A LITTLE DEEPER!

WELL, IF YOU'RE SET ON BEING HUMAN...

"...THERE'S ONLY ONE WAY!"

GUMBO, GUMBO IN THE POT, WE NEED A PRINCESS, WHATCHA' GOT?

CHARLOTTE?! SHE'S NOT A PRINCESS, BUT...

...HER FATHER IS **KING** OF THE MARDI GRAS! SO THAT MAKES HER **A PRINCESS!**

CHARLOTTE'S A PRINCESS...DOES THAT COUNT?

YES! BUT ONLY 'TIL MIDNIGHT, WHEN MARDI GRAS IS OVER!

GET HER TO KISS YOU! ONCE SHE DOES... YOU **BOTH TURN HUMAN!**

AND WHAT ABOUT ME, MAMA?

I WANT TO BE HUMAN SO I CAN PLAY JAZZ!

YOU DIG A LITTLE DEEPER! YOU'LL FIND EVERYTHING YOU NEED!

AFTER LEAVING MAMA ODIE'S, THE FRIENDS CAUTIOUSLY CLIMB ON A **STEAMBOAT**...

BUT...

HEY, GATOR!

BONK

187

TA-TA-TAT

NAVEEN WANTS TO PREPARE SOMETHING SPECIAL FOR **TIANA!**

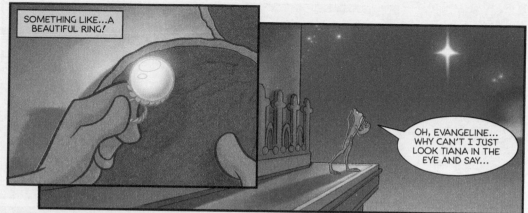

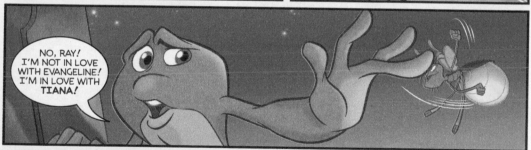

BUT WHEN THAT **MAGIC MOMENT** ARRIVES, TIANA'S ATTENTION IS DRAWN SOMEWHERE ELSE...

THERE IT IS!

YOUR RESTAURANT?

CAN'T YOU PICTURE IT? ALL LIT UP...

...BUT IF I DON'T DELIVER THAT MONEY **FIRST THING** TOMORROW, I'LL LOSE THIS PLACE FOREVER.

TOMORROW?

CLICK

NAVEEN REALIZES HE MUST MARRY CHARLOTTE TO FULFILL TIANA'S DREAM.

TIANA, I LOVE THE WAY YOU LIGHT UP WHEN YOU TALK ABOUT YOUR DREAM!

ALL ASHORE!

I'LL...UH... I'LL GO ROUND UP THE BOYS!

EVANGELINE, I'VE ALWAYS BEEN SO SURE ABOUT WHAT I WANTED, BUT NOW... WHAT DO I DO?

IN THAT VERY MOMENT, THE **SHADOWS** CAPTURE NAVEEN...

...AND BRING HIM SWIFTLY TO FACILIER!

GRAB

GET YOUR HANDS OFF ME!

HOLD STILL, YOUR EMINENCE!

L-LAWRENCE!?

YES, LAWRENCE! NOW, REFILLING THE TALISMAN, SO HE CAN BECOME THE **FAKE PRINCE NAVEEN** AGAIN!

MEANWHILE...

RAY, HAVE YOU SEEN NAVEEN?

LOOK AT YOU...WHERE'S THE RING?

WHAT ARE YOU TALKING ABOUT?

WELL, IF CAP DIDN'T SAY ANYTHING, I'M NOT GOING TO SAY ANYTHING!

RAY?

OKAY! CAP'S NOT GOING TO MARRY CHARLOTTE! HE'S IN LOVE **WITH** YOU!

UH-OH... I SAID TOO MUCH!

YOU SAID JUST ENOUGH, RAY!

BUT WHEN TIANA FINDS HIM, NAVEEN IS ABOUT TO MARRY CHARLOTTE! AND SHE DOESN'T KNOW HE'S **NOT** THE TRUE PRINCE!

OH, NO! HOW CAN YOU STILL BE A FROG? MAMA ODIE SAID--

TIANA, WAIT! WHERE ARE YOU GOING?

SHE RUNS AWAY, DEVASTATED, TO THE CEMETERY...

IT'S TOO LATE...

THIS CAN'T BE RIGHT! I'LL GO BACK AND FIND THE TRUTH!

RAY GETS BACK AND SEES SOMETHING FUNNY NEAR LAWRENCE--A **MOVING** BOX!

?

IS THAT YOU, CAP?!

RAY! GET ME OUT OF THIS BOX!

THANK YOU, RAY!

SPROING

HEY!

OH, GOODNESS GRACIOUS!

THUMP

GRAB

DON'T... DON'T WORRY, CHARLOTTE! I JUST NEED A MOMENT TO COMPOSE MYSELF!

LAWRENCE! WHY ARE YOU DOING THIS?

AS PAYBACK FOR YEARS OF HUMILIATION!

YOU... FINISH THIS DEAL!

POOF

HEY! GIVE ME THAT!

STOMP

I GOT IT!

LET GO OF THAT!

STAY OUT OF SIGHT, LAWRENCE!

RAY FLIES AWAY WITH THE **SHADOWS** FOLLOWING HIM CLOSELY...

SOON THE BRAVE FIREFLY REACHES TIANA AND GIVES HER THE TALISMAN...

...AND BEGINS TO FIGHT THE SHADOWS WITH HIS **LIGHT**!

TIANA, YOU CAN'T LET DR. FACILIER GET THIS! NOW RUN!

BUT...

SCIAFFF!

RAY!

OH, RAY...

NOW, FACILIER AND HIS SHADOWS HAVE CORNERED TIANA...

BACK OFF! OR I'LL BREAK THIS THING INTO A MILLION PIECES!

... SO, HE TRIES TO **TEMPT** HER, SHOWING HER A **DREAM**!

JUST LOOK AT THIS PLACE, DARLIN'!

HER RESTAURANT! AND SHE'S HUMAN AGAIN!

ALL YOU'VE GOT TO DO TO MAKE THIS A REALITY IS HAND OVER THAT TALISMAN TO ME...

NO... THIS ISN'T RIGHT...

DON'T FORGET YOUR POOR DADDY...

MY DADDY NEVER DID GET WHAT HE WANTED...BUT HE HAD WHAT HE NEEDED!

HE NEVER LOST SIGHT OF WHAT WAS REALLY IMPORTANT! AND NEITHER WILL I!

DR. FACILIER'S SHADOW CATCHES THE TALISMAN'S SHADOW AND PREVENTS THE ACTUAL TALISMAN FROM BREAKING.

THE VISION DISAPPEARS AND TIANA TRANSFORMS BACK INTO A FROG.

THUD

SLAP

HEY! GIVE ME THE TALISMAN BACK!

AND FINALLY...

NO! MY PLANS, MY MONEY, MY...

TUM TUM TUM

OH! M-MY FRIENDS! I NEED JUST A LITTLE MORE TIME!

NO! NOOO! NOOO!

AND THE SHADOW MAN IS **LOST IN THE SHADOWS** FOREVER!

AND LAWRENCE? HE'S IN BIG TROUBLE, TOO!

BOYS, DRAG THIS MAGGOT DOWN TO THE PRISON!

MEANWHILE, AFTER NAVEEN'S EXPLANATION, CHARLOTTE AGREES TO MARRY HIM AND HELP TIANA.

I AM DOING THIS BECAUSE... SHE'S MY EVANGELINE.

SHE'S ABOUT TO KISS HIM, WHEN...

WAIT! DON'T DO THIS!

TIANA! BUT... IT'S THE ONLY WAY TO GET YOU YOUR DREAM!

MY DREAM WOULDN'T BE COMPLETE... WITHOUT YOU!

I LOVE YOU, NAVEEN!

OH! ALL MY LIFE I'VE READ ABOUT TRUE LOVE... TIANA. YOU'VE FOUND IT!

I'LL KISS YOU! NO MARRIAGE REQUIRED!

DING

DING

BUT THE CLOCK STRIKES MIDNIGHT... IT'S TOO LATE!

DING

DING

SMACK

SMACK

DING

DING

OH, I'M SO SORRY...

TIANA! NAVEEN!

LOUIS, WHAT IS IT?

IT'S RAY. HE'S HURTING VERY BAD.

FROM THAT DAY ON, THINGS GET BETTER AND BETTER.

TIANA'S DREAM COMES TRUE. SHE FINALLY OWNS HER BEAUTIFUL, WELCOMING RESTAURANT!

EUDORA IS THE HAPPIEST MOTHER, BECAUSE TIANA'S THE HAPPIEST DAUGHTER.

LOUIS IS JUMPING AND JIVING ALL DAY AND ALL NIGHT LONG!

AND RAY?

OH, RAY'S REALLY HAPPY...

...BECAUSE NOW HE'S NEXT TO HIS EVANGELINE...

...SHINING SIDE BY SIDE!

AND TIANA AND NAVEEN LIVED HAPPILY EVER AFTER!

The End

Aladdin

"AHHH-- SALAAM AND GOOD EVENING TO YOU, WORTHY FRIEND!"

"PLEASE, PLEASE, COME CLOSER..!"

KJN007/D92222

WELCOME TO AGRABAH... CITY OF MYSTERY...

...OF ENCHANT- MENT...

...OF THE FINEST MERCHANDISE THIS SIDE OF THE RIVER JORDAN!

PERHAPS A BEAUTIFUL ANTIQUE POT...

PERHAPS YOU WOULD BE MOST REWARDED TO CONSIDER--

--THIS!

DO NOT BE FOOLED BY ITS COMMONPLACE APPEAR- ANCE! LIKE SO MANY THINGS, IT IS NOT WHAT IS OUTSIDE, BUT WHAT IS INSIDE, THAT COUNTS!

THIS LAMP ONCE CHANGED THE COURSE OF A YOUNG MAN'S LIFE--A YOUNG MAN WHO HIMSELF WAS NOT QUITE WHAT HE SEEMED...

PERHAPS YOU WOULD LIKE TO HEAR THE TALE?

"IT BEGINS ON A DARK NIGHT...

"...WHERE A DARK MAN WAITS...

"...WITH A DARK PURPOSE...!"

YOU ARE LATE.

WOW...

YOU MUST BE *HUNGRY*, LITTLE BOY!

UH-- HUH!

HERE YOU GO!

YOU'D BETTER BE ABLE TO *PAY* FOR THAT!

I DON'T HAVE ANY *MONEY*--

DO YOU KNOW WHAT THE *PENALTY* IS FOR *STEALING*?!

PLEASE--IF YOU LET ME GO TO THE *PALACE*, I CAN GET MONEY FROM THE *SULTAN!*

THANK YOU, KIND SIR! I'M SO GLAD YOU *FOUND* HER!

WHAT ARE YOU DOING?!

JUST *PLAY* ALONG!

YOU *KNOW* THIS GIRL?

SADLY, YES. SHE IS MY *SISTER.*

SHE'S A LITTLE *CRAZY!*

SHE *SAID* SHE KNEW THE *SULTAN!*

SHE THINKS THE *MONKEY* IS SULTAN!

O WISE SULTAN, HOW MAY I *SERVE* YOU?

TRAGIC, ISN'T IT? BUT NO HARM DONE!

C'MON, SIS-- TIME TO GO SEE THE *DOCTOR!*

WHY, HELLO, DOCTOR!

HEY-- *PUT THOSE BACK!*

RUN!

EEEK!

COME BACK HERE, YOU LITTLE *THIEVES!*

LATER, IN JAFAR'S SECRET LAB...

WITH ALL DUE *RESPECT,* YOUR ROTTENNESS ≥PANT PANT!≤ COULDN'T WE JUST WAIT FOR A ≥PANT PANT!≤ *REAL STORM?!*

SAVE YOUR *BREATH,* IAGO. *FASTER!*

YES, O MIGHTY EVIL ONE!

PART, SANDS OF TIME! REVEAL TO ME THE ONE WHO CAN *ENTER* THE CAVE!

YES...YES! THERE HE *IS--*

--MY *DIAMOND* IN THE *ROUGH!*

I'LL HAVE THE *GUARDS* EXTEND HIM AN *INVITATION* TO THE *PALACE...*

THAT EVENING...

THIS IS WHERE YOU LIVE?

YEP, JUST ME AND ABU. WE COME AND GO AS WE PLEASE. IT'S NOT MUCH, REALLY--

--BUT IT'S GOT A GREAT VIEW! THE PALACE LOOKS PRETTY AMAZING, HUH?

OH, YES... WONDERFUL...

I WONDER WHAT IT WOULD BE LIKE TO LIVE THERE... TO HAVE SERVANTS AND VALETS...

SURE. PEOPLE WHO TELL YOU WHERE TO GO AND HOW TO DRESS...

THAT'S BETTER THAN HERE! YOU'RE ALWAYS SCRAPING FOR FOOD AND DUCKING THE GUARDS...

YOU'RE NOT FREE TO MAKE YOUR OWN CHOICES... WHAT TO DO, WHO TO MARRY...

SOMETIMES YOU FEEL SO--

YOU'RE JUST SO--

--TRAPPED!

HERE YOU ARE!

PRINCESS JASMINE! WHAT ARE YOU DOING *OUTSIDE* THE *PALACE?*

THAT'S *NOT* YOUR CONCERN! *RELEASE* HIM!

I WOULD, PRINCESS--BUT MY ORDERS COME FROM *JAFAR!* YOU'LL HAVE TO TAKE IT UP WITH *HIM!*

AND SO...

PRINCESS, HOW MAY I BE OF *SERVICE?*

THE *GUARDS* JUST TOOK A BOY FROM THE *MARKET*-- ON *YOUR* ORDERS!

YOUR FATHER HAS *CHARGED* ME WITH KEEPING *PEACE* IN AGRABAH!

THE BOY WAS A *CRIMINAL!*

WHAT WAS HIS *CRIME?*

WHY, KIDNAPPING THE *PRINCESS*, OF COURSE!

OH, DEAR. SADLY, THE BOY'S *SENTENCE* HAS ALREADY BEEN CARRIED OUT!

BUT HE *DIDN'T* KIDNAP ME! I *RAN AWAY!*

WHAT SENTENCE?

DEATH... BY BEHEADING.

oh!

SO HOW'D IT GO?

I THINK SHE TOOK IT RATHER *WELL!*

AND OUTSIDE...

OH, *RAJAH,* =SOB= THIS IS ALL *MY* FAULT!

I DIDN'T EVEN KNOW HIS *NAME...*

LATER THAT NIGHT, AND NOT SO FAR AWAY...

SHE WAS THE *PRINCESS!* I CAN'T *BELIEVE* IT, ABU! I MUST'VE SOUNDED *SO STUPID* TO HER!

SHE'S GONNA MARRY A *PRINCE...* AND *I'M* A *FOOL...*

YOU'RE ONLY A *FOOL* IF YOU *GIVE UP,* BOY!

WHO ARE *YOU?*

A LOWLY *PRISONER,* LIKE YOURSELF. BUT *TOGETHER,* PERHAPS WE CAN BE SOMETHING *MORE!*

THERE IS A *CAVE,* BOY, FILLED WITH *TREASURES* BEYOND YOUR *WILDEST* DREAMS! TREASURE ENOUGH TO IMPRESS EVEN YOUR *PRINCESS,* I'D WAGER...

JAFAR, HURRY UP! I'M *DYIN'* IN HERE!

SHH!

SO WHY WOULD YOU SHARE ALL THIS TREASURE WITH *ME?*

I NEED A YOUNG PAIR OF *LEGS* AND A STRONG *BACK* TO GO IN AFTER IT!

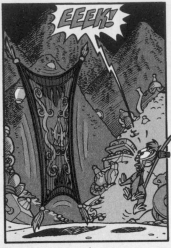

EEEK!

A...A MAGIC CARPET! HEY, MAYBE HE CAN HELP!

CARPET, WE'RE TRYING TO FIND THIS LAMP—

I THINK HE KNOWS WHERE IT IS!

THERE'S THE LAMP, UP THERE IN THE LIGHT!

WAIT HERE.

THIS IS IT?

THIS IS WHAT WE CAME ALL THE WAY DOWN HERE TO—

ABU--**NOOO!**

INFIDELS! YOU HAVE TOUCHED THE FORBIDDEN TREASURES!

NOW YOU SHALL NEVER AGAIN SEE THE LIGHT OF DAY!!

FOOOSH!

WHHHISSSSSSHHHHH!

THANKS, CARPET! LET'S MOVE!

WHOOOA!

EEEK!

RUN, ABU! GO ON!!

227

ENOUGH ABOUT *YOU*, CASANOVA! TALK ABOUT *HER*!

THE HAIR, THE EYES-- *PICK A FEATURE!*

UH, PRINCESS JASMINE, YOU'RE VERY... UHH...

SPLENDID, WONDERFUL, MAGNIFICENT, GLORIOUS, PUNCTUAL--

PUNCTUAL! ER... *BEAUTIFUL!*

NICE RE-COVERY!

I'M *RICH*, TOO. A FINE PRIZE FOR ANY *PRINCE* TO MARRY.

RIGHT. A PRINCE LIKE *ME.*

RIGHT. A PRINCE LIKE *YOU...*

...AND EVERY OTHER *STUFFED-SHIRT*, SWAGGERING PEACOCK I'VE MET!

OH--GO *JUMP OFF A BALCONY!!*

YANK!

MAYDAY! MAYDAY! CRASH AND BURN! STOP HER!

YOU'RE *RIGHT.* YOU SHOULD BE *FREE* TO MAKE YOUR OWN *CHOICE.*

I'LL GO NOW...

WAIT-- *NO!*

HOW... HOW ARE *YOU DOING* THAT?

IT'S A MAGIC *CARPET!* YOU DON'T WANT TO GO FOR A *RIDE*, DO YOU?

WELL, YOU KNOW... *ROYALTY* GOING OUT INTO THE CITY IN *DISGUISE*... IT SOUNDS A LITTLE *STRANGE*, DON'T YOU THINK?

NOT *THAT* STRANGE...

ONCE BACK AT THE PALACE...

GOOD NIGHT, MY *HANDSOME PRINCE.*

BUMP!

SLEEP WELL, PRINCESS.

≡SIGH!≡ FOR THE *FIRST TIME* IN MY *LIFE,* THINGS ARE STARTING TO GO *RIGHT!*

HUH--?!?

I'M AFRAID YOU'VE *WORN OUT* YOUR *WELCOME*, PRINCE ABOOBOO.

GUARDS, MAKE *SURE* HE IS NEVER *FOUND*.

THE CLIFFS OVERLOOKING THE SEA ARE *HIGH*---

SPLASH!

---AND THE WATERS ARE *DEEP*---

---BUT *STILL* THERE IS *HOPE!*

RUB!

IT *NEVER* FAILS---YOU GET IN THE *BATH* AND THERE'S A *RUB* AT THE *LAMP!*

---MM... MM...

AGH! AL! KID, SNAP *OUT* OF IT!

YOU CAN'T *CHEAT* ON THIS ONE! I CAN'T *HELP* YOU UNLESS YOU MAKE A WISH! SAY, "*GENIE, I WANT YOU TO SAVE MY LIFE!*" GOT IT??

LATER, AS DAWN BREAKS...

SULTAN... ...THEY WANT ME TO BE SULTAN...

HUZZAH! HAIL THE CONQUERING HERO! WHOOP-WHOOP-WHOOOP!

ALADDIN, YOU'VE JUST WON THE *HEART* OF THE *PRINCESS!* WHAT ARE YOU GOING TO DO NEXT?

PSSST! YOUR LINE IS, "I'M GOING TO *FREE* THE *GENIE!*"

GENIE.... I *CAN'T.*

LOOK, I'M *SORRY,* I REALLY AM! BUT THEY WANT TO MAKE ME *SULTAN!* AND WITHOUT *YOU,* I'M JUST... ALADDIN.

BUT, AL--YOU *WON!*

BECAUSE OF *YOU!* THE ONLY REASON ANYBODY THINKS I'M WORTH *ANYTHING* IS BECAUSE OF *YOU!* WHAT IF JASMINE FINDS OUT THE TRUTH? SHE'LL HATE ME!

GENIE, I *NEED* YOU. I CAN'T WISH YOU FREE.

FINE. I *UNDERSTAND.* AFTER ALL, YOU'VE *LIED* TO EVERYONE *ELSE.* HEY, I WAS BEGINNING TO FEEL *LEFT OUT.*

MEANWHILE, IN JAFAR'S SECRET LABORATORY...

AT LAST, THE *LAMP*...THE *GENIE*...THE *POWER*...IS *MINE!!*

YOU KNOW, AL, I'M GETTING *REALLY*--

AIIIEEEE!! I DON'T THINK YOU'RE HIM!

HAVEN'T I SEEN YOUR *PICTURE* IN THE *POST OFFICE*--*SIDE VIEW?!*

I AM YOUR *MASTER* NOW!

I WAS *AFRAID* OF THAT...

NOW, GENIE, GRANT ME MY *FIRST* WISH!

I WISH TO RULE ON HIGH AS *SULTAN!*

PEOPLE OF AGRABAH--MY DAUGHTER HAS *FINALLY* CHOSEN A *SUITOR!* A MAN OF *INTEGRITY!* A MAN WHO IS *EXACTLY* WHAT HE *APPEARS* TO BE--

--PRINCE *ALI ABABWA!*

YIPPEE!

YEAH!

OH, BOY...

SHREKK!

FATHER--?!?

WH--WHAT IS GOING ON?!

SNOW. WIND. DESOLATION.

THE *ENDS* OF THE EARTH...

ABU?

ABU?!

ABU, ARE YOU OKAY?

I'M SORRY. I'VE MADE A MESS OF *EVERYTHING.* I SHOULD HAVE FREED THE GENIE WHEN I HAD THE *CHANCE.*

I'VE GOT TO GO BACK AND SET THINGS *RIGHT!* SOMEHOW...

CARPET! YOU'RE *HERE!*

EEEK!!

ALL RIGHT! BACK TO AGRABAH, LET'S *GO!*

LATER, IN THE PALACE HIGH ATOP THE MOUNTAIN---

IT *PAINS* ME TO SEE YOU *REDUCED* TO THIS, JASMINE.

A BEAUTIFUL DESERT BLOOM SUCH AS *YOURSELF* SHOULD BE ON THE ARM OF THE MOST *POWERFUL* MAN IN THE *WORLD!*

THEREFORE, I HAVE DECIDED TO MAKE MY *FINAL* WISH!

GENIE, I WISH FOR *PRINCESS JASMINE* TO FALL *DESPERATELY* IN *LOVE* WITH ME!

246

GRIMSBY! GRIM! C'MERE, QUICK!

I JUST *SAW* SOMETHING!

IT WAS INCREDIBLE! IT LOOKED LIKE A GIRL, BUT SHE HAD A TAIL LIKE A FISH AND--

AYE, THAT WAS A *MERMAID* YE WERE SEEIN'! NOW THOSE ARE A GLORIOUS PEOPLE--

OH, *RUBBISH.* GIVE ME A MOMENT TO--

AH! *THERE* WE ARE. LOOK HERE, ERIC. LOOK AT YOUR MERMAID.

WHAT THE HECK IS *THAT,* GRIM?!

THAT, ERIC, IS A MANATEE. YOUR "MERMAID."

NOW DON'T BE EMBARRASSED, ERIC. MISTAKES CAN HAPPEN TO *ANYONE*--EVEN A *PRINCE.*

ARF! ARF!

HUSH NOW, MAX!

COME NOW, ERIC. WE'LL GO BELOW AND CONTINE WITH YOUR STUDIES ON NAVAL HISTORY.

AND WE'LL HAVE NO MORE NONSENSE ABOUT MERMAIDS.

ARF! ARF!

BUT THERE WERE MANY YEARS OF HOPING, DREAMING AND ADVENTURING BEFORE HER LIFE ON LAND BEGAN, YEARS SUCH AS THIS ONE--WHEN SHE HAD JUST TURNED FIFTEEN--

AND A LIFE ABOVE THE WAVES WAS A MERE FANTASY. AS MUCH OF A FANTASY TO THE GIRL, WHO LIVED ON THE OCEAN FLOOR, AS HER OWN EXISTENCE WOULD BE TO THOSE WHO LIVED ON PARQUET FLOORS.

FOR, WHEN ALL WAS SAID AND DONE, THEY WERE STILL THE FORBIDDEN HUMANS. AND SHE, OF COURSE, WAS...

DISNEY'S
THE LITTLE MERMAID

ARIEL! ARIEL!

AW, *C'MON, ARIEL!* YOU *KNOW* YOU'RE NOT SUPPOSED TO BE UP HERE!

OH, I'M NOT *HURTING* ANYONE, FLOUNDER! I WAS JUST LOOKING.

BUT YOU'RE NOT EVEN SUPPOSED TO DO *THAT!*

FLOUNDER, THAT'S SO *SILLY.* WHAT IS THERE SO TERRIBLE IN THE WORLD THAT YOU CAN'T EVEN *LOOK* AT IT?

HUMANS! I HEARD THAT...THAT JUST THE SIGHT OF 'EM, *uh,* MAKES YOUR EYEBALLS MELT!

AND YOUR BRAIN GETS ALL FROZEN OVER, AND, AND, AND YOUR *TONGUE* FALLS OUT, AND...

THANKS FOR THE FAVOR, MANNY.

ANYTIME YOU NEED ME, PRINCESS.

...AND YOUR SCALES GET ALL BROWN AND *YUCKY,* AND...

WELL, THAT'S WHAT *I* HEARD!

FLOUNDER, YOU CAN BE SUCH A GUPPY.

I'M *NOT* A GUPPY.

THEN DON'T *ACT* LIKE ONE.

"MELTING EYEBALLS." HONESTLY!

WELL, *THAT'S* WHAT--

YOU HEARD, I KNOW.

BUT I'M *TIRED* OF JUST HEARING THINGS. I WANT TO *SEE* THEM. EXPERIENCE THEM FIRST-HAND!

CAN'T YOU EXPERIENCE THEM FIRST-HAND BY LISTENING TO STORIES ABOUT THEM?

IT DOESN'T *WORK* THAT WAY, FLOUNDER.

WHERE IS DAT GIRL?!

SHE *KNEW* WE HAD REHEARSAL TODAY! WHAT DOES SHE T'INK SHE'S *DOING*--

--CAUSING ME GRIEF LIKE DIS?!

OH, YOU KNOW HOW IT IS WITH ARIEL. SHE JUST GETS INVOLVED WITH THINGS AND, WELL ... *YOU* KNOW.

DAT GIRL *CANNOT* GO THROUGH LIFE WIT' YOU MAKING EXCUSES FOR HER ALL DA TIME, ALANA!

SHE GOT TO LEARN TO STAND UP ON HER OWN TWO FINS! IF YOUR *FATHER* HEARS ABOUT DIS . . .

DADDY HAS BUSINESS AWAY, AND HE LEFT ME IN CHARGE. SO HE'S NOT GOING TO FIND OUT.

UNLESS SOMEBODY TELLS HIM, RIGHT, AQUATA?

OH, ARISTA, YOU *WOULDN'T*...!

WELL, I DON'T SEE WHY *WE* SHOULD ALWAYS HAVE TO SHOW UP FOR CHOIR REHEARSALS AND LITTLE ARIEL *GETS* TO DO WHATEVER SHE *WANTS*.

OR ARE YOU JUST AFRAID THAT DADDY WILL BE DISAPPOINTED IN HIS ELDEST GIRL BECAUSE HE LEFT YOU IN CHARGE OF RUNNING THE KINGDOM ... AND YOU COULDN'T EVEN KEEP TRACK OF ONE MERMAID?

ARISTA, YOU CAN BE SUCH A *SEA URCHIN* SOMETIMES.

WELL, DA SEA KING WON'T HEAR ABOUT DIS FROM *ME*...BUT DON'T EXPECT ME TO COVER FOR DAT GIRL WHEN WE HAVE A PERFORANCE AND WE SOUND FLATTER DAN A STARFISH! DAT'S ALL I GOT TO SAY!

I JUST DON'T SEE WHY WE SHOULD HAVE TO OBEY THE RULES, AND ARIEL JUST FLITS AROUND.

ARISTA CAN BE A REAL TATTLE FISH-TAIL, BUT SHE'S ALSO RIGHT. FATHER TRUSTED ME TO BE CHARGE. I'M SUPPOSED TO BE RESPONSIBLE.

HOW CAN I BE A FUTURE RULER WHEN I CAN'T EVEN GET MY OWN *SISTERS* TO RESPECT ME?

ARIEL, *WAIT!* WE'RE NOT SUPPOSED TO COME *OUT* THIS FAR!

THERE'S BOUNDARIES YOUR FATHER SET! OFFICIAL *BORDERS!* AND WE'RE ABOUT TO CROSS ONE! WE'LL BE OUTSIDE OF THE MERPEOPLE TERRITORY!

NOW THERE YOU GO *AGAIN,* FLOUNDER!

BORDERS ARE JUST MADE-UP *LINES!* LOOK DOWN THERE. DO *YOU* SEE ANY LINES?

WELL, AH... NO.

THERE, Y' SEE?

WHY SHOULD I WORRY ABOUT IMAGINARY LINES? AM I AN IMAGINARY *MERMAID?*

ALL THAT MATTERS ARE THE THINGS YOU CAN *SEE,* FLOUNDER!

YOU HAVE TO KEEP YOUR EYES OPEN, NOT CLOSE THEM IN FEAR!

RULES ARE FINE FOR WHEN YOU'RE LITTLE AND DON'T KNOW ANY BETTER. BUT I'M *NOT* A CHILD ANYMORE.

JUST BECAUSE DADDY SAYS THIS AND THAT AND *WHATEVER,* DOES THAT MEAN I DON'T HAVE A MIND OF MY *OWN?* I'M OLD ENOUGH TO MAKE MY OWN RULES AND DO WHAT *I* THINK IS *RIGHT* AND WHAT I *FEEL* LIKE DO--

--IIIIINNNNGGG!

MAY... MAYBE NOW MIGHT BE A GOOD TIME TO LEAVE, AT THAT.

YEAH. *YEAH*, I HEAR MY *MOM* CALLING. *THAT'S* IT. I KNEW I HEARD SOMETHING. LET'S GO.

RIGHT.

WHA-WHAT'S HAPPENING?!

I DON'T KNOW! MAYBE THEY'RE ALL SCARED OF SOMETHING THAT'S COMING AFTER THEM?! BUT I DON'T KNOW WHAT! MAYBE A WHALE OR--

ARIEL, WOULD I BE A GUPPY IF I SAID I THINK WE BETTER GET OUT OF HERE FAST?

NOT IN THE LEAST!

GOOD!

OOHHHH, MY--!

WHAT'S WRONG?!

KEEP GOING! *DON'T* LOOK BACK! JUST *KEEP GOING!*

LOOK OUT!!

UNNHHHH!

WE'RE CAUGHT! WE'RE CAUGHT! ARIEL, WHAT'RE WE GONNA DO? WE'RE GONNA GET COOKED AND EATEN! I'M TOO YOUNG TO FRY!

I'LL TELL YOU WHAT I'M GONNA DO...

I'M GOING TO GET YOU OUT OF HERE!

UNH! UNNHHHH..

THERE!

GO, FLOUNDER! GO!

BUT WHAT ABOUT YOU?!

DON'T WORRY ABOUT ME! I GOT MYSELF INTO THIS--

AND I'LL GET MYSELF OUT!!

HOLY HALIBUT!

I THOUGHT WE'D BEEN CAUGHT BY HUMANS OR SOMETHING! BUT THOSE AREN'T HUMANS!

I'VE NEVER SEEN ANYTHING LIKE THESE PEOPLE. THEY'RE LIKE US, BUT... HALF-EEL! I'VE NEVER HEARD OF A PEOPLE LIKE THAT...

...OR A *CITY* LIKE THAT!

DOWN *HERE!* BRING IT DOWN *HERE!*

OKAY! DUMP THEM IN HERE!

HURRY IT *UP!* COME ON!

I'M NOT ALL WEDGED IN BY THE FISH ANYMORE!

I CAN MOVE MY ARMS AGAIN! JUST NEED A SECOND TO--

I DID IT!

OOOOPS...

uhh... HELLO.

EEEYAAAAAHHHHH!!

HUH?

THEY'RE... THEY'RE AFRAID OF ME.

ME?!

UH-OH.

THERE! THERE IT IS! I TOLD YOU!

CATCH IT! CATCH IT!

IT'S GETTING AWAY!!

STOP IT BEFORE IT KILLS SOMEONE!!

"IT?" "KILLS SOMEONE?" WHAT DO THEY THINK I AM, ANYWAY?

MOMMY! MOMMY! MAKE IT GO AWAY!

THIS IS CRAZY! THEY'RE ALL ACTING LIKE I'M SOME SORT OF MONSTER!

I CAN'T *BELIEVE* DIS IS HAPPENING! HALF-*SERPENTS*, YOU SAID?! DIS ISN'T ONE OF YOUR *STORIES* NOW, IS IT?

DO I *LOOK* LIKE I'M MAKING THIS UP?!

NO, YOU LOOK TERRIFIED. OH, MON. I DID *NOT* NEED DIS.

BREAKING DA LAW. GOING BE-YOND DA BOUNDARIES. WHAT DID DAT GIRL T'INK SHE WAS *DOING?*

IF HER *FATHER* FINDS OUT...

OHHH, HE'D BE FURIOUS, AND DAT'S A FACT. I HATE TO ADMIT HOW MUCH I LIKE DAT GIRL... SO BEAUTIFUL, WID A *LOVELY* VOICE...

IF ONLY SHE USED DA *HEAD* DAT DA VOICE CAME IN EVERY NOW AND DEN...

SO YOU'LL *HELP?*

WHY ME? WHY ARE YOU DRAGGING *ME* INTO DIS?

BECAUSE YOU'RE THE ONLY GROWN-UP I FELT COMFORTABLE GOING TO, SINCE YOU'RE THE ONLY ONE *SMALLER* THAN I AM. IF I SAY *THAT*, YOU'LL JUST GET MAD...

BECAUSE, *uh*, YOU'RE THE *SMARTEST* ONE AROUND, SEBASTIAN, AND YOU'RE SO *CREATIVE* AND EVERY-THING, I FIGURED, IF *ANYONE'S* GOT THE IMAGINATION TO GET ARIEL OUT OF THIS, IT'S *YOU!*

DIS IS TRUE.

NOW *THAT'S* ODD. I CAN'T RECALL EVER SEEING SEBASTIAN AND FLOUNDER HANGING ABOUT WITH EACH OTHER...

YET THERE THEY ARE... AND GOING SOMEPLACE IN AN AWFUL *HURRY.*

I'LL BET IT HAS SOMETHING TO DO WITH ARIEL. THAT'S THE ONLY THING THAT COULD GET FLOUNDER MOVING THAT QUICKLY.

THEN AGAIN, WHAT IF I'M *WRONG?* AM I SUPPOSED TO ASSIGN MEN TO FOLLOW THEM, AND IT TURNS OUT TO BE NOTHING? AND THEY'LL SAY, "THERE'S AQUATA AGAIN, PANICKING AS ALWAYS. SOME *RULER-IN-TRAINING* SHE IS."

FATHER WOULDN'T FEEL THE NEED TO GET HELP. HE'D SEE WHAT WAS GOING ON *PERSONALLY.*

AND THAT'S EXACTLY WHAT I'M DOING. BESIDES, WHATEVER ARIEL'S GOTTEN HERSELF MIXED UP IN...

"I'M SURE *I* CAN GET HER OUT OF IT."

LET ME *OUT* OF HERE.

YOU *SEE*, FATHER? I TOLD YOU SHE COULD SPEAK.

INCREDIBLE. JUST *INCREDIBLE.*

WHO COULD HAVE THOUGHT IT POSSIBLE? A CREATURE OF MYTH, RIGHT IN *FRONT* OF US.

YOU CAN UNDERSTAND WHAT I'M SAYING?

OF *COURSE* I CAN!

ALL RIGHT, THESE ARE MY PARENTS, THE KING AND QUEEN--*CORNELIUS* AND *AEMELIA.* MY NAME IS CELIA. I'M THE PRINCESS HERE, AND YOUR NEW OWNER.

NOBODY'S MY "OWNER." I'M ARIEL, I BELONG TO MYSELF, AND YOU HAVE NO BUSINESS KEEPING ME PRISONER HERE.

AND WHERE DO YOU COME FROM, ARIEL-WHO-BELONGS-TO-HERSELF?

FROM BEYOND THAT BIG CHASM WITH THE DARK WATER.

YOU'RE *LYING!* BEYOND THE CHASM IS JUST NOTHINGNESS! EVERY MORAY CHILD KNOWS THAT, THERE'S NO LIFE BEYOND THERE! IT'S DEATH TO EVEN TRY AND GO THERE!

MORAY? WHAT'S A *MORAY?*

WE ARE THE *MORAY.* AND MY DAUGHTER IS RIGHT. EVERY CHILD KNOWS THERE'S NO LIFE BEYOND THERE...

AND YET, WE CAN'T DENY THAT HERE YOU *ARE.* WHICH MEANS THAT THERE MAY INDEED BE MORE TO THE LEGENDARY HORROR STORIES OF HALF-FISH PEOPLE THAN WE CREDITED.

HORROR STORIES--?

OH, YES. SAVAGE, FREAKISH *CREATURES* THAT MAKE YOUR EYEBALLS MELT AND YOUR BRAIN FREEZE OVER AND YOUR *TONGUE* FALL OUT. MERE STORIES-- BUT THEN AGAIN, MAYBE NOT.

SO HOW MANY *MORE* OF YOU ARE THERE?

IF I TELL THEM ABOUT MY FAMILY...ABOUT MERMAID CITY...WHO KNOWS WHAT THEY'LL DO?

WE'RE NOT EXPECTING ANY KIND OF INVASION. WE'D GET *SLAUGHTERED!*

I HATE TO LIE, BUT I'VE GOT TO PROTECT MY PEOPLE.

ACTUALLY... I'M THE ONLY ONE OF MY KIND.

I WAS BORN IN THE SEA. MY MOTHER WAS A *DOLPHIN.* SHE DIED WHEN I WAS VERY YOUNG, AND NEVER TOLD ME ABOUT WHERE I CAME FROM. I NEVER KNEW *WHO* MY FATHER WAS.

YOU MIGHT SAY MY BIRTH WAS...

...SOMETHING OF A *FLUKE.*

OHHHH, GEE. I KNOW SEBASTIAN SAID WE COULD COVER MORE TERRITORY THIS WAY...SPLITTING UP AND SEARCHING THE CITY FOR ARIEL, AND THEN MEETING UP AGAIN. BUT I REALLY, *REALLY* HATE THIS.

I COULD GET CAUGHT AT ANY TIME, AND THEN WHO KNOWS WHAT COULD...

UH-OH. MORE OF THOSE HUNTER GUYS. THEY REALLY MAKE MY BLOOD RUN WARM.

AW, NO! I DON'T *BELIEVE* IT! THEY *CAUGHT--!*

DID YOU HEAR SOMETHING? LIKE A YELP?

YOU BEEN *WORKIN'* TOO HARD! THAT'S YOUR PROBLEM.

OHHH, THIS IS JUST GETTING WORSE AND WORSE! *NOW* WHAT AM I GONNA DO?

THIS IS THE SERPENTINE CELEBRATION, ARIEL. ONE OF OUR MOST *POPULAR* EVENTS...

...IT CELEBRATES THE STRENGTH AND SKILL OF OUR HUNTERS AND WARRIORS. THEY NEED SOMETHING TO KEEP THEMSELVES SHARP... ESPECIALLY SINCE WE HAVE NO *ENEMIES* TO FIGHT.

OF COURSE, THAT WOULD *CHANGE* IF THERE WERE ANOTHER UNDERSEA RACE TO CONQUER. A PITY YOU'RE ONE OF A KIND.

I HOPE THOSE WEIGHTS AREN'T *TOO* UNCOMFORTABLE. BUT WE COULDN'T TAKE THE CHANCE OF YOU JUST SWIMMING OFF, COULD WE?

OH, CERTAINLY *NOT.*

WHAT HAPPENS IS, WE RELEASE OUR BEST HUNTERS INTO THE SERPENTINE MAZE WITH JUST SIMPLE KNIVES, AND THEY HAVE TO HUNT DOWN AND KILL A VERY SPECIAL TYPE OF BEAST THAT WE CAPTURED JUST FOR THE OCCASION, BEFORE THE BEAST KILLS *THEM,* OF COURSE.

SOUNDS CHARMING.

DOESN'T IT, THOUGH? AND WE HAVE SENTINELS WHO KEEP THE NET *HEAVILY* ELECTRIFIED SO THAT NO ONE CAN ESCAPE.

THIS YEAR, HOWEVER, SOMETHING HAS JUST COME UP. SO BEFORE WE RELEASE THE HUNTERS, WE'VE DECIDED TO GIVE THE BEAST A BIT OF A *SNACK.*

AH. *THERE'S* THE SNACK NOW.

THAT "OTHER MERMAID" IS AQUATA... AND IF I DON'T DO SOMETHING, MY SISTER IS DEAD! WHAT'S SHE DOING HERE, ANYWAY?

THIS IS WONDERFUL. THE NEXT TIME I DECIDE I WANT TO TRY AND HELP ARIEL, I'M JUST GOING TO STAY-

--HOME?

YEEOOWWHOAA!!

AQUATA!!

AHA! FATHER, DID YOU HEAR? SHE CALLED HER BY A NAME! ARIEL *DOES* KNOW HER! SHE--

STOP! COME HERE IMMEDIATELY!

GET HER! SHE'S TRYING TO HELP THE OTHER ONE!

DON'T *CONCERN* YOURSELF, CELIA. THE LEAD WEIGHTS WON'T LET HER GET FAR...

AND THE GUARDS ARE KEEPING THE NET ELECTRIFIED, SO SHE CAN'T POSSIBLY GET THROUGH.

COME ON! THE SHOUTING'S COMING FROM OVER *THIS* WAY! I BET THAT'S WHERE SHE IS!

YOU SURE YOU SAW DEM WID AQUATA IN DE NETS?

POSITIVE! THAT'S WHEN I WENT TO FIND YOU!

OH, MON! IT'S ONE CATASTROPHE AFTER ANOTHER WIT' DOSE GIRLS! NEXT TIME YOU WANT TO FIND ME, FLOUNDER, DON' LOOK SO HARD!

WHAT'S GOING ON? EVERYONE'S SHOUTING AND YELLING, AND I DON'T SEE--

HIGHNESS... HOW WOULD *YOU* FEEL IF CELIA WERE IN *MY* SITUATION? CAPTURED, HELD FAR AWAY FROM HOME? STUCK IN A ZOO SOMEWHERE?

WELL, I...TERRIBLE, I IMAGINE.

YEAH! SO JUST IMAGINE HOW KING TRITON'S GONNA FEEL WHEN HE FINDS OUT *HIS* DAUGHTER IS HERE--

KING TRITON! SO THIS IS A *PRINCESS* THEN! HER FATHER IS SOMEONE OF POWER!

OOOOOOPS!!

NICE GOING, FLOUNDER.

IF *THAT'S* THE CASE, THEN ALL I HAVE TO DO IS USE HIS DAUGHTER AS A BARGAINING CHIP...AND I COULD TAKE HIS ENTIRE KINGDOM!

CELIA, YOU HAVE DONE MORE *EXCELLENTLY* THAN I COULD HAVE *IMAGINED*.

THANK YOU, FATHER!

I'M *SORRY*, ARIEL.

COME! LET'S *CELEBRATE!*

I KNOW WHAT YOU MEAN, YOUR HIGHNESS. SO AM I.

GEE, ARIEL, ME AND MY BIG MOUTH...

OH, IT'S *OKAY*, FLOUNDER. CHANCES ARE THAT, SOONER, OR LATER, THEY WOULD HAVE...

Hmmm? WHAT'S THAT IN MY--

AW, IT'S JUST THAT *THINGAMABOB* YOU PICKED UP.

Ohhh, YEAH. I'D FORGOTTEN I--

Hmmm...

WHAT *IS* IT, ARIEL? YOU GOT AN *IDEA?*

YOU KNOW... I JUST *MIGHT.*

FLOUNDER, IF WE GET *OUT* OF HERE, YOU KNOW WHAT THE *FIRST* THING I'LL DO IS?

ESCAPE.

AFTER THAT.

NO. WHAT?

APOLOGIZE TO MY FATHER FOR GOING WHERE HE SAID I *SHOULDN'T.*

I'M SORRY, YOUR MAHJESTY!!

IT'S ALL MY FAULT! I SHOULD NEVER HAVE LEFT HER BEHIND!

SO WHAT IF I GOT A BIG ENOUGH SHOCK TO STOP A WHALE! CRABS ARE MADE OF *STERNER STUFF!*

I'M A DISGRACE TO DE OCEAN FLOOR! I'M DA LOWEST OF DE LOW! I'M--

SEBASTIAN, IT'S *NOT* YOUR FAULT.

WHEW! WELL, *DAT'S* GOOD TO KNOW.

SEBASTIAN WAS SIMPLY TRYING TO COVER FOR ME, FATHER.

DAT IS TRUE. BECAUSE DAT IS DE WAY I AM.

I *BUNGLED* IT, FATHER. YOU LEFT ME IN CHARGE WHILE YOU WERE AWAY ON BUSINESS OUTSIDE THE KINGDOM...

AND I COME BACK TO FIND ARIEL GONE, SEBASTIAN IN HYSTERICS, AND YOU TELLING ME ABOUT YOU AND YOUR SISTER CAPTURED BY THE *MORAY...*

THE MORAY? IS *THAT* THEIR NAME, FATHER? YOU KNOW WHO THEY ARE?

OF *COURSE* I DO, AQUATA. I'M THE KING OF THE SEA. I'M NOT EXACTLY UNINFORMED.

YOU RETURNED HERE AND LEFT ARIEL BEHIND, AQUATA. WHY DID YOU DO THAT?

--THEN PERHAPS NONE OF US WOULD HAVE THE CHANCE AGAIN. I THOUGHT BEING IN CHARGE MEANT DOING WHATEVER YOU *WANTED*. I NEVER REALIZED THAT, SOMETIMES, BEING IN CHARGE MEANS HAVING TO DO THINGS YOU'D MUCH RATHER *NOT* DO.

BECAUSE I DIDN'T HAVE ENOUGH RESOURCES TO HANDLE THINGS. AND IF I DIDN'T ESCAPE WHEN I HAD THE CHANCE--

I FAILED YOU, FATHER. I APOLOGIZE. AND I'D UNDERSTAND IF YOU NEVER LEFT ME IN CHARGE AGAIN.

FAILED ME? YOU TOOK RESPONSIBILITY, BLAMED NO ONE ELSE FOR THINGS THAT WENT WRONG, AND LEARNED A VALUABLE TRUTH OR TWO. *WHERE'S* THE FAILURE IN THAT?

AS FOR LEAVING YOU IN CHARGE...

THAT'S EXACTLY WHAT I'M GOING TO DO *AGAIN*, RIGHT NOW. I'LL RISK NONE OF MY PEOPLE, OR MORE OF MY DAUGHTERS, AGAINST THOSE SERPENTS.

I'LL ATTEND TO THE MORAY MYSELF.

OAT'S RIGHT, DE KING IS GOING TO SHOW DEM WHAT'S WHAT. OH, WHAT I'D GIVE TO SEE DAT...

I'M GLAD YOU FEEL THAT WAY, SEBASTIAN...

BECAUSE YOU'RE COMING ALONG.

EEEEP!

DEAD! WHAT DO YOU MEAN, THE SERPENTINE MONSTER IS DEAD?!

IT COULD NOT BE HELPED, YOUR HIGHNESS!

THE CREATURE WAS SO BERSERK FROM EVERYTHING THAT HAD HAPPENED--NOT TO MENTION BEING DEPRIVED OF HIS PREY--

THAT IT WAS IMPOSSIBLE FOR US TO TAKE HIM ALIVE. HE FOUGHT MUCH TOO FIERCELY IN HIS AGITATED STATE.

TO USE LESS THAN LETHAL FORCE AGAINST THE SERPENTINE WOULD HAVE MEANT THE LIVES OF MANY HUNTERS.

YES, YES. YOU'RE RIGHT, OF COURSE. BESIDES, I WOULDN'T WANT TO RISK LOSING ANY OF MY HUNTERS OR SOLDIERS NOW.

NOT WHEN I WILL NEED THEM IF WE GO TO WAR WITH THE MERPEOPLE.

WHAT SHALL WE DO WITH THE BODY OF THE SERPENTINE, HIGHNESS? WITH THE FESTIVAL ENDING PREMATURELY--

OH, I'LL BE MORE THAN HAPPY TO TAKE IT OFF YOUR HANDS.

BY THE DARK WATER--!

WHO ARE *YOU*?! HOW DID YOU GET IN HERE?!

WHY, MY *DEAR* KING OF THE MORAY... I'M THE *SEA WITCH*. AND WHEN I WANT TO GO SOMEPLACE, I GENERALLY GET THERE.

HIGHNESS, SHOULD WE...?

LET HER PASS. NO MATTER WHAT HER APPEARANCE, *I'M* NOT AFRAID OF ANY WOMAN.

WELL HOW *FORTUNATE*... CONSIDERING I'M NOT JUST *ANY* WOMAN.

MY, YOU ARE A *STURDY* ONE, AREN'T YOU? ENOUGH TO GIVE KING TRITON *QUITE* A FIGHT, I'D WAGER.

YOU KNOW KING TRITON?

DARLING, IF *I* DON'T KNOW IT, IT HASN'T HAPPENED. AND I'LL BE HAPPY TO FILL YOU IN ON ALL SORTS OF INFORMATION ABOUT TRITON.

ENOUGH THAT, IF YOU USE IT CORRECTLY, YOU COULD BECOME RULER OF THE SEVEN SEAS.

BUT I WANT SOMETHING FROM YOU IN RETURN.

ARIEL! HERE SHE COMES!

YOU KNOW I DON'T WANT TO TELL YOU WHAT TO DO, MY DEAR, BUT--

THEN DON'T TRY, MOTHER. I DON'T HAVE TO LISTEN TO YOU. I *KNOW* WHAT I'M DOING!

GOOD DAY, YOUR HIGHNESS.

SO! LEARNING HOW TO ADDRESS ME FINALLY, *eh?*

I WAS TALKING TO YOUR MOTHER.

HOW RESPECTFUL. PERHAPS THERE IS ONE ADVANTAGE TO ARIEL BEING HERE AFTER ALL. PERHAPS *YOU* CAN LEARN SOMETHING FROM HER, CELIA.

YOU ALWAYS DID TAKE A BIT TOO MUCH AFTER YOUR FATHER.

Hmph!

"LEARN SOMETHING FROM HER." LIKE *WHAT*? HOW TO BE A PRISONER?

LIKE HOW TO APPRECIATE YOUR MOTHER WHEN YOU HAVE ONE.

OH, AND I SUPPOSE YOU'RE ALWAYS PERFECT AND POLITE WHEN DEALING WITH YOUR ELDERS. WITH YOUR "KING TRITON."

OH, I WOULDN'T SAY *THAT*.

BUT EVEN WHEN I DISAGREE WITH HIM, I'M NOT RUDE WITH HIM THE WAY YOU ARE. I WAS BROUGHT UP *BETTER* THAN THAT.

I *SEE*. INSTEAD OF SAYING WHAT YOU THINK, YOU *ACT* RESPECTFUL AND THEN DO WHAT YOU WANT ANYWAY BEHIND HIS BACK.

YOU BET THAT'S WHAT SHE DOES! AND...

uhh...

...I'LL JUST WAIT OVER HERE AND STAY QUIET.

THANK YOU.

GUESS WHAT, MY DEAR PRISONER. IT LOOKS LIKE YOUR FATHER AND I ARE--

HEY! WHAT ARE YOU DOING TO THE GLASS?

NOW, ARIEL! NOW!

WAAP!

OOOOOFF!

HOW DARE YOU! I'M A ROYAL PERSONAGE!

WHAT YOU ARE IS A ROYAL PAIN!

I'LL SHOW YOU! I DON'T NEED MY GUARDS TO HANDLE YOU, YOU UPSTART!

OW! STOP THAT!!

ZZZZT!

295

SEBASTIAN... *STOP...*

...HELPING...

...ME!

YES, YOUR MAJESTY.

HIS POWER IS *INCREDIBLE!* I'M EXHAUSTED... BUT I'VE *STILL* GOT THE UPPER HAND...

GIVE UP, TRITON. I'VE *STILL* GOT YOUR DAUGHTER...

OH, *NO,* YOU DON'T. I'VE GOT *YOUR* DAUGHTER HIDDEN AWAY...

WHERE SHE'S BEING TORTURED AND ALL *KINDS* OF STUFF...

AND UNLESS YOU SURRENDER AND PROMISE TO LEAVE THE MERPEOPLE *ALONE,* WELL ... I CAN'T BE RESPONSIBLE FOR WHAT HAPPENS TO HER.

SHE *MEANS IT,* CORNELIUS.

AEMELIA! YOU, TOO, WOULD--

ALL RIGHT! *GO!* I SWEAR, I SHALL LEAVE YOU BE! JUST GO! I'VE PROVEN MY SUPERIORITY THIS DAY, ANYWAY!

OH, REALLY?

TAKE A LOOK AROUND.

NOOOO! STTTTOPPPP!

STOP SINGING!! STOP IT!

HERE'S ONE YOU'LL LOVE. LISTEN... ♪YO HO YO HO,♪ ♪A PIRATE'S LIFE FOR ME♪♪!

THANKS FOR WATCHING HER, SCUTTLE. I'LL TAKE IT FROM HERE.

ALL RIGHT, "PRINCESS." YOU WON THIS ONE. BUT YOU CAN BET YOU HAVEN'T HEARD THE LAST OF THIS.

I WOULDN'T THROW AROUND THREATS IF I WERE YOU. REMEMBER... SCUTTLE KNOWS LOTS OF SONGS.

WELL, SHE'S AN OBNOXIOUS YOUNG THING. AS FOR YOU, YOUNG LADY... I'M RELIEVED YOU'RE SAFE. HOWEVER...

OH, DADDY, I'M SO SORRY. YOU MADE A RULE, AND I IGNORED IT FOR NO GOOD REASON. BUT I'VE LEARNED FROM THIS. REALLY. AND FROM NOW ON, I'LL NEVER DISOBEY ANOTHER RULE...

UNLESS IT'S FOR A GOOD REASON.

YES... I MEAN, NO! NO, I WOULDN'T EVER! NOT--

WE'LL DISCUSS IT FURTHER, ARIEL... AT HOME.

YES, DADDY.

"YES, DADDY." THE GOOD LITTLE THING. HAAWWW HAW HAW!

I KNEW THAT FOOL CORNELIUS COULD NEVER CONQUER TRITON, AND EVEN IF HE'D HAD, EVEN IF HE'D OBTAINED THE TRIDENT AND CROWN AS I TOLD HIM TO, I'D STILL HAVE BEEN ABLE TO TRICK HIM OUT OF IT. BUT NO MATTER...

...TRITON HAS HIS DAUGHTER, CORNELIUS HAS A CITY TO REBUILD, AND I....

...THANKS TO THE BODY OF THE SERPENTINE MONSTER... HAVE A NEW HOME.

I SO LOVE A HAPPY ENDING.

HA HA HA HA HA

fin

IN A FAR AWAY
LAND LONG AGO LIVED
A KING AND A QUEEN,
WHO WERE VERY SAD
SINCE THEY DIDN'T
HAVE CHILDREN.

FINALLY, THEIR WISH WAS GRANTED:
THE QUEEN HAD A DAUGHTER AND THEY
CALLED HER AURORA.

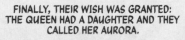

A GREAT HOLIDAY WAS PROCLAIMED THROUGHOUT
THE KINGDOM SO THAT EVERYONE MIGHT PAY
HOMAGE TO THE INFANT PRINCESS.

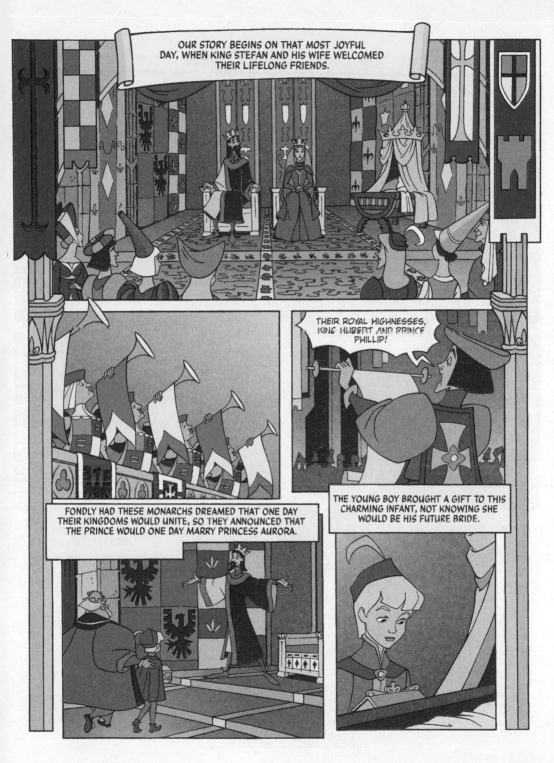

OUR STORY BEGINS ON THAT MOST JOYFUL DAY, WHEN KING STEFAN AND HIS WIFE WELCOMED THEIR LIFELONG FRIENDS.

THEIR ROYAL HIGHNESSES, KING HUBERT AND PRINCE PHILLIP!

FONDLY HAD THESE MONARCHS DREAMED THAT ONE DAY THEIR KINGDOMS WOULD UNITE, SO THEY ANNOUNCED THAT THE PRINCE WOULD ONE DAY MARRY PRINCESS AURORA.

THE YOUNG BOY BROUGHT A GIFT TO THIS CHARMING INFANT, NOT KNOWING SHE WOULD BE HIS FUTURE BRIDE.

WHEN THE HERALDS ANNOUNCED THE GOOD NEWS, A SWEET LIGHT FILLED THE ROOM...

THEIR MOST HONORED AND EXALTED EXCELLENCIES, THE THREE GOOD FAIRIES!

MISTRESS FLORA, MISTRESS FAUNA, AND MISTRESS MERRYWEATHER!

SHE'S SO *NICE!*

YOUR MAJESTIES! EACH OF US MAY BLESS THE CHILD WITH A SINGLE GIFT!

CHARMING PRINCESS, *MY* GIFT SHALL BE THE GIFT OF *BEAUTY!*

MY GIFT SHALL BE THE GIFT OF *SONG!*

BUT JUST BEFORE MERRYWEATHER PRESENTS HER GIFT...

DON'T DESPAIR, YOUR MAJESTIES. MERRYWEATHER STILL HAS *HER* GIFT TO GIVE!

BUT CAN SHE UNDO THIS FEARFUL CURSE?

OH! NO, SIRE. MALEFICENT HAS POWERS WE DON'T HAVE. BUT SHE CAN HELP!

SWEET PRINCESS, A SPINDLE WILL PRICK YOUR FINGER SINCE *MALEFICENT* CAST THIS SPELL ON YOU! BUT YOU *WON'T* DIE, AND THIS IS WHAT WILL HAPPEN...

...YOU WILL FALL *ASLEEP*, AND THIS SLEEP WILL LAST FOR A LONG TIME. AFTER A HUNDRED YEARS YOU SHALL WAKE WHEN YOU ARE KISSED BY A CHARMING *PRINCE!*

BUT KING STEFAN, STILL FEARFUL FOR HIS DAUGHTER'S LIFE, DID THEN AND THERE DECREE THAT EVERY SPINNING WHEEL IN THE KINGDOM SHOULD BE BURNED! SO IT WAS DONE...

AND SO FOR 16 YEARS THE WHEREABOUTS OF THE PRINCESS REMAINED A MYSTERY, WHILE DEEP IN THE FOREST IN A WOODCUTTER'S COTTAGE THE GOOD FAIRIES CARRIED OUT THEIR WELL-LAID PLAN. LIVING LIKE MORTALS, THEY HAD REARED THE CHILD AS THEIR OWN. THEY CALLED HER BRIAR ROSE.

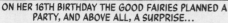

ON HER 16TH BIRTHDAY THE GOOD FAIRIES PLANNED A PARTY, AND ABOVE ALL, A SURPRISE...

I THINK THIS DRESS IS IDEAL, ISN'T IT?

THIS IS THE ONE *I* PICKED, TOO! SHE'LL LOOK BEAUTIFUL IN THAT!

I THOUGHT ABOUT A FEW CHANGES.

WE'LL MAKE IT BLUE!

OH, NO! IT SHOULD BE *PINK*.

WHAT ARE YOU UP TO?

MEANWHILE, IN THE FOREST, AURORA IS WALKING WITH HER FRIENDS, THE ANIMALS.

I WOULD LIKE TO SING ABOUT LOVE AS THE BIRDS DO.

NOT FAR AWAY FROM HERE, PRINCE PHILLIP IS TAKING HIS DAILY RIDE.

YOU HEAR THAT, SAMSON? WHAT A *BEAUTIFUL* VOICE!

LET'S FIND OUT WHO IT IS. YOU'LL HAVE AN EXTRA BUCKET OF OATS AND A FEW...

...CARROTS?

HEY, NOT SO QUICK!

AUNT FLORA, AUNT FAUNA, AUNT MERRYWEATHER, WHERE ARE YOU?

OH!

HAPPY BIRTHDAY!

OH! YOU DARLINGS, IT'S THE MOST BEAUTIFUL DAY OF MY LIFE! EVERYTHING'S SO WONDERFUL! I'M SURE YOU WILL LIKE HIM!

DID YOU SPEAK TO A *STRANGER?*

HE'S NOT A STRANGER, I SAW HIM ONCE UPON A DREAM!

SHE'S IN *LOVE!*

OH!

THIS IS TERRIBLE!

BUT I'M 16! I CAN!

IT ISN'T *THAT*, DEAR! YOU'RE ALREADY BETROTHED!

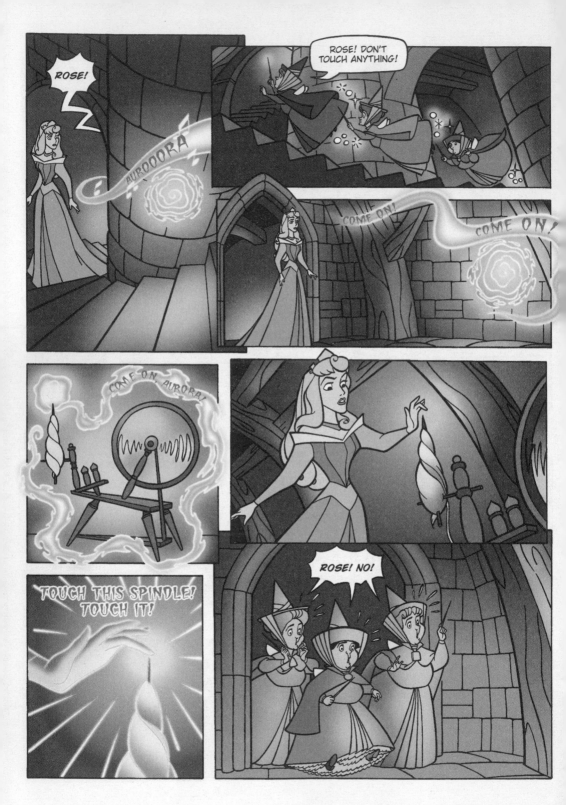

I'VE JUST BEEN TALKING TO PHILLIP. →YAWN!← HE'S FALLEN IN LOVE...

...WITH A PEASANT GIRL!

WITH A PEASANT GIRL!

AND THE PEASANT GIRL? WHO IS SHE? WHERE DID HE MEET HER?

ONCE UPON A DREAM! →YAWN!←

ONCE UPON A DREAM! OH, ROSE! PRINCE PHILLIP!

OH, NO! WE'RE TOO *LATE!*

MALEFICENT! SHE HAS PRINCE PHILLIP AT THE FORBIDDEN MOUNTAINS!

WHAT TO DO? WE CAN'T *GO* THERE, CAN WE?

BUT WE *MUST!*

THE YEARS ROLLED BY, BUT NOW, AT LONG LAST, THE VALIANT PRINCE IS COMING ON HIS NOBLE STEED TO WAKE HIS LOVE WITH TRUE LOVE'S KISS AND PROVE THAT TRUE LOVE CONQUERS ALL!

HA! HA!

EVIL *WITCH!*

?!

COME, MY PET! LET US LEAVE OUR NOBLE PRINCE WITH THESE HAPPY VISIONS!

CAW!
CAW!
CAW!

CAW!
CAW!

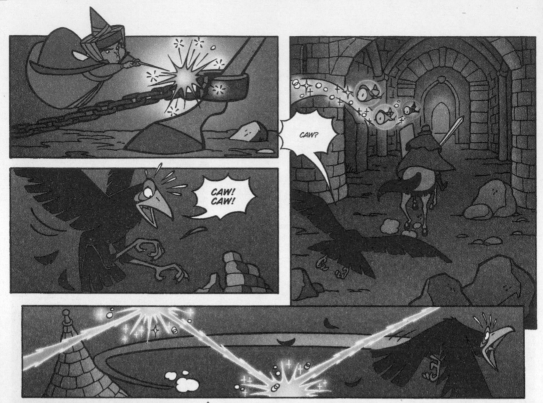

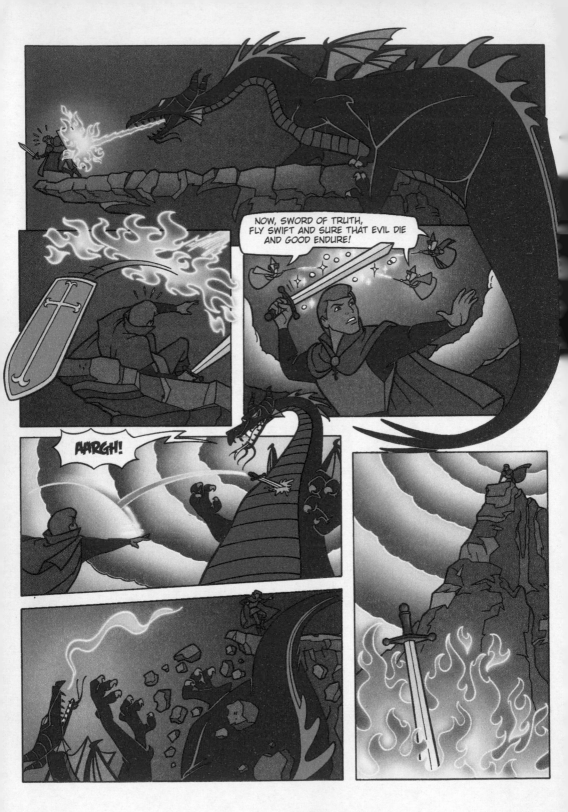

COME, PRINCE!

SHE'S WAITING FOR YOU!

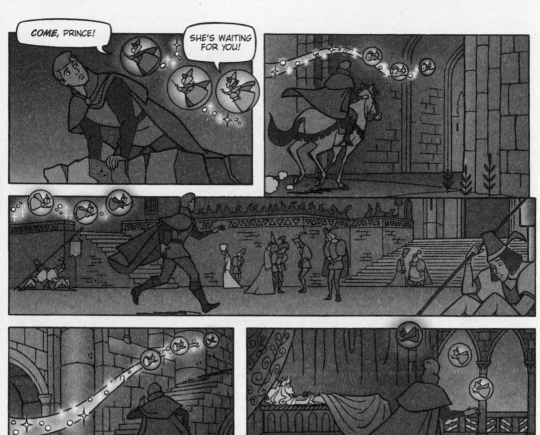

The End

FWIP

NOW, WAKE UP THE ANCESTORS.

OK, PEOPLE! RISE AND SHINE! YOU'RE *WAY* PAST THAT BEAUTY SLEEP THING! TRUST ME!

BONG BONG BONG

LET A *GUARDIAN* BRING HER HER BACK.

YES, AWAKEN THE MOST *CUNNING*.

NO, THE *SWIFTEST*.

SILENCE! WE MUST SEND THE MOST *POWERFUL* GUARDIAN!

OK, OK, I GET THE PICTURE. *I'LL GO!*

I KNEW MULAN WAS A TROUBLEMAKER!

SHE GOT IT FROM YOUR SIDE OF THE FAMILY!

HEE! HA! HA! HA! YOU HAD YOUR CHANCE TO PROTECT THE FAMILY... YEAH. THANKS A LOT! HEE!

AND YOUR POINT IS...

YOU ARE NOT WORTHY. NOW, AWAKEN THE GREAT STONE DRAGON!

YO, *ROCKY!* WAKE UP! HELLO-OOO...

UH-OH.

BONG BONG BONG BONK

SNAP

CRUMBLE!!

OH, MAN! THEY'RE GONNA *KILL* ME!

MEANWHILE, INSIDE THE ARMY TENT, GENERAL LI GOES OVER HIS PLANS WITH HIS SON, LI SHANG

I WILL TAKE MY TROOPS TO THE *TUNG-SHAO PASS* AND STOP SHAN-YU BEFORE HE DESTROYS THIS VILLAGE. YOU WILL STAY AND TRAIN THE NEW RECRUITS... *CAPTAIN.*

CAPTAIN? YES, SIR!

SOLDIERS!

HE STARTED IT!

I DON'T NEED ANYONE CAUSING TROUBLE IN MY CAMP. WHAT'S YOUR NAME?

UHHH...*PING!*

LET ME SEE YOUR CONSCRIPTION NOTICE

FA ZHOU. *THE* FA ZHOU? I DIDN'T KNOW FA ZHOU HAD A *SON.*

HE DOESN'T TALK ABOUT ME MUCH.

NEXT MORNING...

ORDER, PEOPLE, ORDER!

I'D LIKE A PAN-FRIED NOODLE!

HOW ABOUT SOME SWEET AND PUNGENT SHRIMP?

MOO GOO GAI PAN!

LOOKS LIKE RICE BOY SLEPT IN THIS MORNING.

HUNGRY, PING? I STILL OWE YOU A KNUCKLE SANDWICH.

THAT'S NOT FUNNY!

~OOF!~

WE'VE GOT A *LONG* WAY TO GO.

THE RECRUITS TRAIN, DAY...

...AFTER DAY...

...AFTER GRUELING DAY.

YOU'LL *NEVER* BE A FIT SOLDIER. PACK UP AND GO HOME.

BUT MULAN ISN'T READY TO GIVE UP.

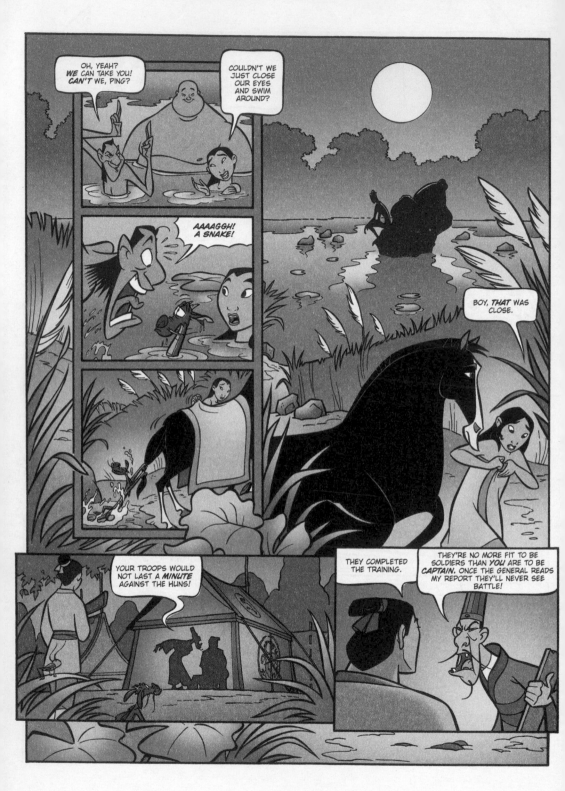

KA-BOOM!

HYAAA!

HEY, GUYS, I'VE GOT AN IDEA...

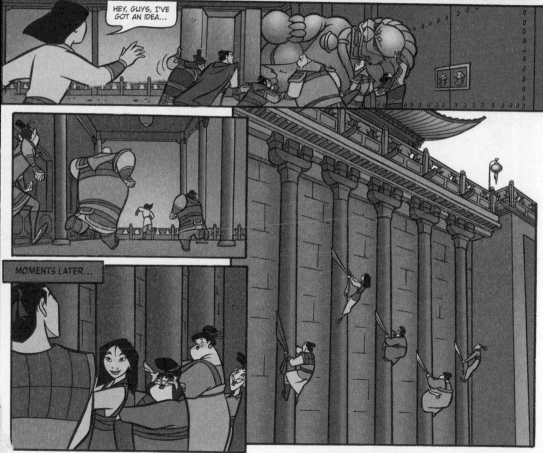

MOMENTS LATER...

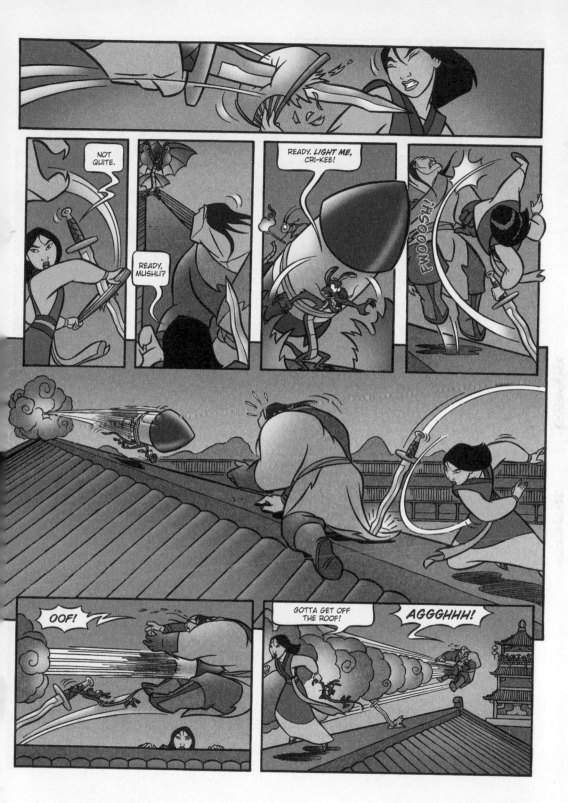

CHI FU, SEE TO IT THAT THIS WOMAN IS MADE A MEMBER OF MY COUNCIL.

WHAT?! AHH... UHHH...

WITH ALL DUE RESPECT, YOUR EXCELLENCY, I'VE BEEN AWAY FROM HOME LONG ENOUGH.

THEN TAKE THIS, SO YOUR FAMILY WILL KNOW WHAT YOU HAVE DONE FOR ME.

AND THIS, SO THE WORLD WILL KNOW WHAT YOU HAVE DONE FOR CHINA.

UM... YOU'RE A... YOU FIGHT WELL.

OH... THANK YOU.

UH-OH.

KLANG!

THIS MIGHT TAKE ME A MINUTE OR TWO...

GET BACK *DOWN* HERE, YOU MANGY CANARD...

EITHER YOU GET OUT OF ZIS KITCHEN ON YOUR *OWN*...

...OR ON A PLATTER WITH ORANGE SAUCE! ZEE CHOICE, SHE IS *YOURS!!*

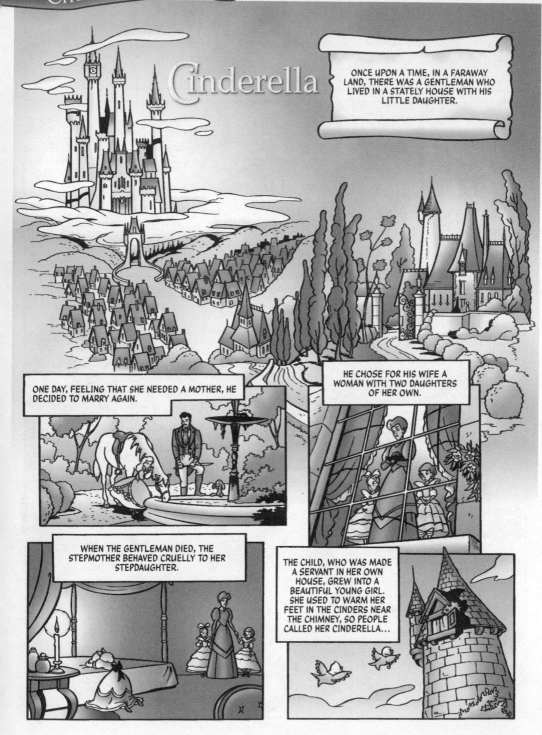

Cinderella

ONCE UPON A TIME, IN A FARAWAY LAND, THERE WAS A GENTLEMAN WHO LIVED IN A STATELY HOUSE WITH HIS LITTLE DAUGHTER.

ONE DAY, FEELING THAT SHE NEEDED A MOTHER, HE DECIDED TO MARRY AGAIN.

HE CHOSE FOR HIS WIFE A WOMAN WITH TWO DAUGHTERS OF HER OWN.

WHEN THE GENTLEMAN DIED, THE STEPMOTHER BEHAVED CRUELLY TO HER STEPDAUGHTER.

THE CHILD, WHO WAS MADE A SERVANT IN HER OWN HOUSE, GREW INTO A BEAUTIFUL YOUNG GIRL. SHE USED TO WARM HER FEET IN THE CINDERS NEAR THE CHIMNEY, SO PEOPLE CALLED HER CINDERELLA...

398

THERE'S A *MOUSE* IN THE HOUSE! CAN YOU IMAGINE THAT?!

A *MOUSE?* WHY, WE'LL TAKE CARE OF IT. FIRST, LET'S FIND IT A DRESS...

A *DRESS?* NO, NO, IT ISN'T A GIRL, IT'S A *BOY!*

IT'S IN A TRAP!

IN A *TRAP?* WE MUST GO AND *RELEASE* IT, QUICKLY!

SOON...

OH! POOR THING, IT'S *FRIGHTENED* TO DEATH.

ZUK! ZUK! DON'T BE SCARED. CINDERELLA'S A *FRIEND*, SHE'S VERY *KIND!*

HERE'S A SWEATER...IT'S A LITTLE SNUG, BUT IT'LL HAVE TO DO FOR NOW! I CHRISTEN YOU OCTAVIUS, *GUS* FOR SHORT.

NOW I MUST GET TO WORK. LOOK AFTER HIM, *JAQ*, AND DON'T FORGET TO *WARN* HIM ABOUT THE *CAT!*

HAVE YOU EVER *SEEN* THE CAT? HE *BITES*, HE *CLAWS*, HE'S *SLY!* HE'S FAT! FAT! *FAT!* ZUK ZUK *LUCIFER!*

LUCIFER... KITTY KITTY KITTY!

LUCIFER! WAKE UP, YOU LAZY CAT!

COME ON, HURRY UP, I HAVEN'T GOT ALL DAY!

I'M SORRY HIS ROYAL HIGHNESS DOESN'T ENJOY BEING WOKEN UP FOR BREAKFAST!

I DIDN'T *ASK* FOR YOU TO BE SERVED FIRST THING IN THE *MORNING!*

LUCIFER! LUCIFER!

YES, YES, GUS. LUCIFER'S TERRIBLE!

ZUK! ZUK! GUS *CATCH* LUCIFER!

NO! DON'T!

LUCIFER'S A *MONSTER!* HE'S *EVIL!*

HERE I COME, LUCIFER!

MEEEOOW!

MRRROOWW!

EEEEEEK! A MOUSE!

MOTHER! SHE PUT A *MOUSE* UNDER MY TEACUP!

I'M *SURE* YOU DID IT ON PURPOSE! YOU'LL *PAY* FOR THIS!

CINDERELLA!

YES, MOTHER?

COME HERE!

SO, WE'VE BEEN PLAYING PRACTICAL JOKES? MAYBE WE HAVE TOO MUCH *TIME* ON OUR HANDS. LET ME SEE...THAT BIG CARPET IN THE HALL--*SCRUB IT!* ALL THE WINDOWS--*WASH THEM!* AND THE CURTAINS, THE TAPESTRIES...OH YES! ONE MORE LITTLE THING...

...GIVE LUCIFER HIS *BATH!*

MEANWHILE, AT THE ROYAL PALACE...

I **WON'T** TAKE **NO** FOR AN **ANSWER!** MY SON IS AVOIDING HIS RESPONSIBILITIES. IT'S HIGH TIME HE STARTED A FAMILY!

YOUR MAJESTY, WE JUST HAVE TO BE PATIENT...

I AM BEING **EXTREMELY** PATIENT!

BUT I'M NOT AS YOUNG AS I **WAS,** MY DEAR GRAND DUKE! AND I WANT TO HAVE **GRANDCHILDREN** BEFORE IT'S **TOO LATE!**

THE PRINCE COMES HOME TODAY, DOESN'T HE? WELL, LET'S CELEBRATE HIS RETURN WITH A GRAND BALL!

AND IF ALL THE ELIGIBLE MAIDENS IN THE KINGDOM WERE INVITED, SURELY HE COULD FALL IN LOVE WITH **ONE** OF THEM?!

SAY YES!

YES-YES-YES-YES, SIRE!

I'LL ORGANIZE A BALL FOR--

TONIGHT!

AN URGENT MESSAGE FROM HIS MAJESTY!

A MESSAGE FROM THE *KING?* WHAT CAN IT *BE?*

CINDERELLA! I THOUGHT I TOLD YOU NEVER TO INTERRUPT US!

BUT A LETTER HAS JUST COME FROM THE PALACE!

THE PALACE?!

GIVE IT TO ME! QUICK!

LISTEN! THERE'S GOING TO BE A BALL IN THE PRINCE'S HONOR AND ALL THE ELIGIBLE MAIDENS IN THE KINGDOM ARE INVITED!

HOW WON-DERFUL! I'M JUST MADE TO BE A PRINCESS!

BUT...THAT MEANS *I* CAN GO, *TOO!*

HA HA! CAN YOU SEE HER DANCING WITH THE PRINCE?!

VERY HONORED, YOUR HIGHNESS, WILL YOU HOLD MY BROOM?

BUT...WHY NOT? AFTER ALL, *I'M* PART OF THE FAMILY!

WHY SHOULDN'T YOU GO? AS LONG AS YOU'VE FINISHED ALL YOUR CHORES... AND YOU HAVE A SUITABLE DRESS TO WEAR!

THANK YOU, MOTHER!

MOTHER! DO YOU REALIZE WHAT YOU'VE *SAID?*

YES, OF COURSE...

...I SAID, *"IF."*

OH! SO YOU DID!

HEE HEE HEE!

CINDERELLA'S TOO HAPPY TO REALIZE HER STEPMOTHER HAS TRICKED HER.

LOOK AT THIS LOVELY DRESS! IT BELONGED TO MY MOTHER!

IT'S A BIT OLD-FASHIONED, BUT I CAN ALTER IT.

I COULD COPY ONE OF THESE DESIGNS!

I LOVE IT! *ZUK! ZUK!*

VERY PRETTY! ~SQUEAK! SQUEAK!~

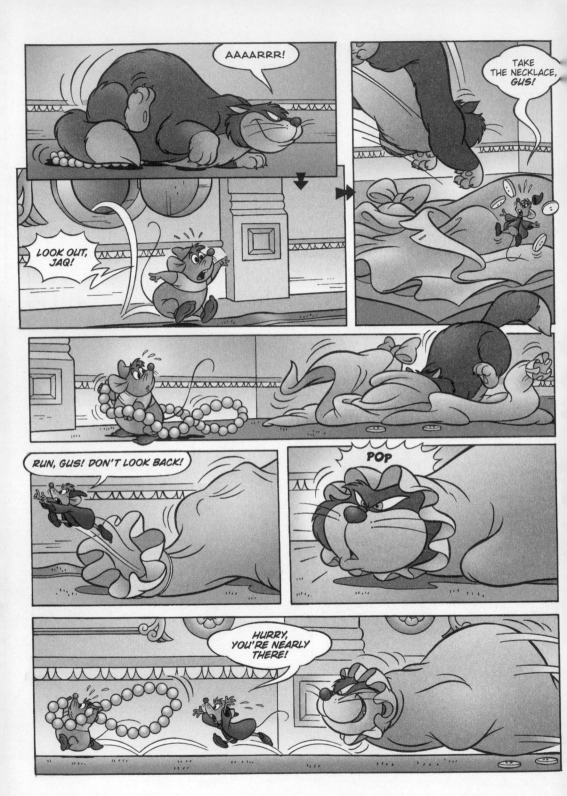

DONG! DONG! DONG! DONG!

THE CARRIAGE IS WAITING!

BUT WHAT'S WRONG? AREN'T YOU READY, CHILD?

I'M NOT GOING TO THE BALL!

WHAT A SHAME! NEVER MIND, THERE'LL BE OTHER OCCASIONS!

OH, WELL. WHAT'S A ROYAL BALL? I'M SURE IT'S DREARY AND BORING AND...COMPLETELY *WONDERFUL!*

WHAT'S THAT?

FOR SUCH AN ELEGANT CARRIAGE, WE NEED... MICE!

MICE?

HA! SWEET LITTLE THINGS. PERFECT!

ABRACADABRA! HEY, PRESTO!

NOW, FOR THE HORSE. AS A COACHMAN, FAITHFUL STEED, TO THE BALL YOUR MISTRESS LEAD!

AND THE DOG! BRUNO, FOR JUST ONE NIGHT, BE A FOOTMAN DRESSED IN WHITE!

EXCUSE ME, BUT DON'T YOU THINK MY DRESS...

OH! GOOD HEAVENS, MY DEAR, JUST LOOK AT THOSE RAGS!

WHAT WAS I THINKING OF? ABRACADABRA! HEY, PRESTO!

NOW, CINDERELLA, REMEMBER--ON THE LAST STROKE OF MIDNIGHT, THE SPELL WILL BE BROKEN AND EVERYTHING WILL BE AS BEFORE. HURRY! THE BALL IS WAITING AND TIME WILL FLY!

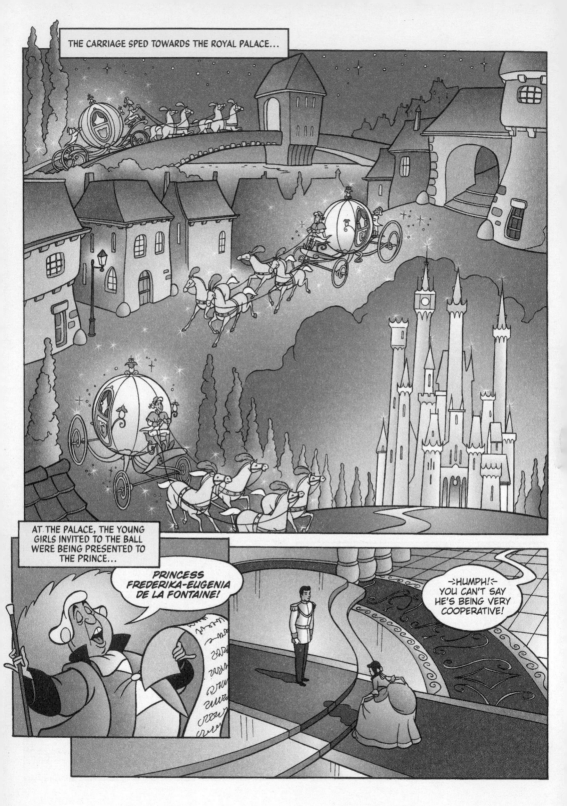

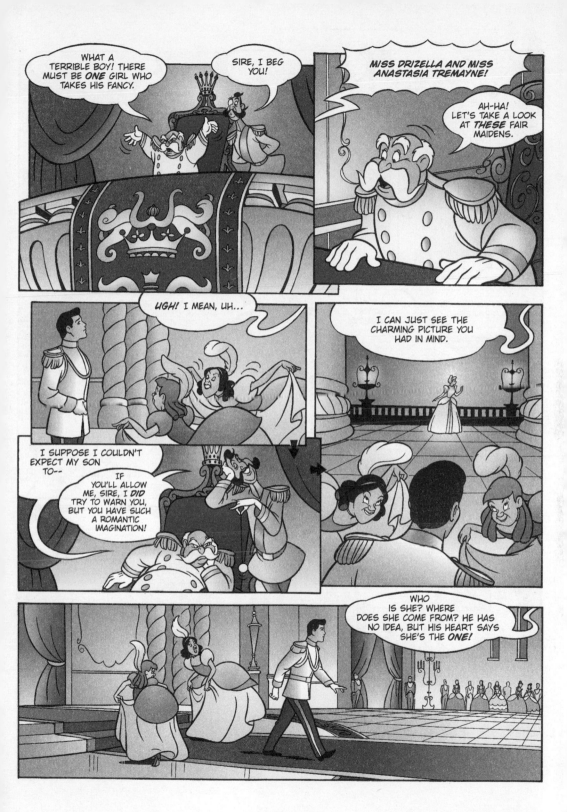

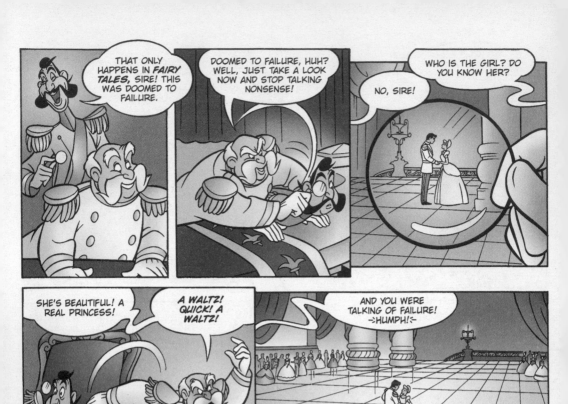

WHO IS SHE, MOTHER? DO WE KNOW HER?

THE PRINCE IS OVERWHELMED!

SHE MUST BE A YOUNG GIRL FROM...

WAIT A MINUTE! I'M SURE I'VE SEEN THAT FACE SOMEWHERE.

SORRY, STATE SECRET!

THE WALTZ LEADS TO A ROMANTIC STROLL...

BUT SUDDENLY...

IT'S MIDNIGHT!

DONG!

GOODBYE!

NO, WAIT! DON'T LEAVE!

DONG!

GOODBYE!

COME BACK! I DON'T EVEN KNOW YOUR NAME! *HOW WILL I FIND YOU?*

DONG!

DONG!

DONG!

DONG!

MY DEAR FRIENDS! I FORGOT EVERYTHING TONIGHT, EVEN THE TIME! BUT IT WAS SO WONDERFUL! HE WAS SO HANDSOME, SO CHARMING, SO GALLANT. OH, WELL, IT'S OVER NOW!

LOOK, CINDERELLA! THE SLIPPER!

OH, THANK YOU! THANK YOU FOR EVERYTHING, DEAR GODMOTHER!

DRIZELLA! ANASTASIA! GET UP! COME ON, *GET UP!*

WHAT'S GOING ON?

YEAH, WHAT'S WRONG WITH HER?

WHAT? I'M STILL SLEEPY!

IT'S THE TALK OF THE KINGDOM! THE GRAND DUKE WILL BE HERE ANY MINUTE!

NOW, LISTEN TO ME. MAYBE ONE OF YOU CAN MARRY THE PRINCE! NO ONE, NOT EVEN THE PRINCE, KNOWS WHO THAT GIRL WAS. HIS ONLY CLUE IS A GLASS SLIPPER AND THE KING HAS ORDERED EVERY MAIDEN IN THE KINGDOM TO TRY IT ON. THE GIRL IT FITS WILL BE THE PRINCE'S BRIDE!

CRASH! DING-BLING!

I'M SORRY, I HEARD WHAT YOU WERE SAYING AND...I DON'T KNOW WHAT CAME OVER ME!

LITTLE FOOL! LEAVE THAT MESS AND COME HELP MY DAUGHTERS WITH THEIR DRESSES!

DRESSES...OH YES, I MUST GET DRESSED FOR THE PRINCE!

LA LA LA LA...SO THIS IS LOVE...

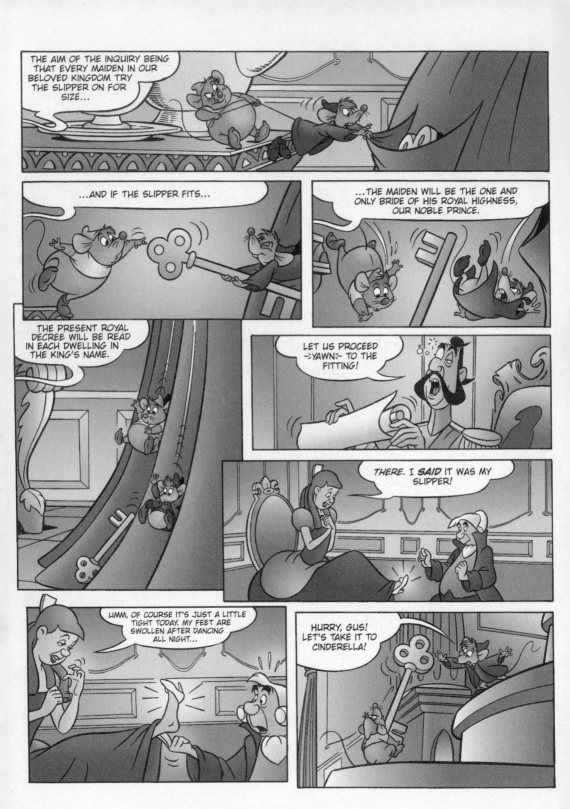

THE AIM OF THE INQUIRY BEING THAT EVERY MAIDEN IN OUR BELOVED KINGDOM TRY THE SLIPPER ON FOR SIZE...

...AND IF THE SLIPPER FITS...

...THE MAIDEN WILL BE THE ONE AND ONLY BRIDE OF HIS ROYAL HIGHNESS, OUR NOBLE PRINCE.

THE PRESENT ROYAL DECREE WILL BE READ IN EACH DWELLING IN THE KING'S NAME.

LET US PROCEED –>YAWN<– TO THE FITTING!

THERE. I *SAID* IT WAS MY SLIPPER!

UMM, OF COURSE IT'S JUST A LITTLE TIGHT TODAY. MY FEET ARE SWOLLEN AFTER DANCING ALL NIGHT...

HURRY, GUS! LET'S TAKE IT TO CINDERELLA!

COME ON, GUS, WE'RE NEARLY THERE!

JUST ONE MORE LITTLE EFFORT!

-»HUF«-
-»HUFFF«-

IT'S UP THERE!

OOOOOH!

MEANWHILE, IN THE DRAWING ROOM, THE FITTING CONTINUES...

YOU CLUMSY DOLT! YOU'RE NOT REALLY TRYING! I HAVE A GOOD MIND TO SLAP YOU!

THAT WILL DO! NEXT YOUNG GIRL!

IS THAT YOU? YOU'VE GOT THE KEY!

YUK! YUK! WE'RE COMING!

MEEEOOOWW!

WHAM

435

OH, *NO!* NO NO *NO!* I'M A *GONER!* THE KING WILL HAVE MY *HEAD!*

YOUR GRACE, I'VE GOT THE *OTHER* SLIPPER!

IT FITS YOU *PERFECTLY,* YOUNG LADY!

HOORAY FOR CINDERELLA! *HOORAY!*

AND SO WE COME TO A FAIRY TALE ENDING...

DING DONG! DING DONG!

LOOK, GUS, IT'S HER! IT'S CINDERELLA!

THANK YOU! THANK YOU FOR EVERYTHING!

AND THEY LIVED HAPPILY EVER AFTER...

DISNEP

Aladdin
THE RETURN of JAFAR

NOT FAR FROM THE CITY OF AGRABAH, THE CALM OF AN ARABIAN NIGHT...

BADOOM DOOM

...IS SMASHED BY THE HOOFBEATS OF GALLOPING STEEDS!

HURRIED HORSEMEN TAKE FLIGHT OVER PLAINS AND PAST OASES, THROUGH NARROW RAVINES...

RUMBLE!

...HEADING STRAIGHT FOR A HIDING SPOT THAT ONLY THEY KNOW—

BLAM

:HEE!: THIS NIGHT HAS BEEN *QUITE* REWARDING. YES, YES...A *DISTINCT* BOOST IN FINANCES HERE!

AS YOU SAY, *ABIS MAL!* HA-HA-HA! NEVER BEFORE HAVE WE STOLEN *SO MUCH!*

LOOKIT THIS STUFF! ISN'T IT *NEAT?* WOULDN'T YOU SAY :HEE-HEE!: MY *COLLECTION'S* COMPLETE?

YOUR COLLECTION, O' LEADER? WE *DIVIDE* THE LOOT--DO WE *NOT?*

OH! YEAH, YEAH...*'COURSE* WE DO! PILES TO GO BEFORE WE SLEEP!

TAKE A LOAD OFF, MEN! *EVERYONE* GETS HIS SHARE!

GLOM

-;HEE-HEE!;- OOK! VOOTIE! VOOTIE!

QUIET, ABU, BEFORE WE'RE SPOTTED!

THEN AGAIN...THEY HAVEN'T NOTICED US YET.

SNATCH

TOO BUSY PLAYING GRAND THEFT AGRABAH OUT THERE!

WITH EACH BIG DUM-DUM EITHER SWIMMING IN LOOT...

...OR PLOTTING TO GRAB SOMEONE ELSE'S!

NNGH!

-;HA!;- WE HAVE GATHERED MUCH WEALTH TONIGHT, NO THANKS TO OUR LEADER!

OOF!

PLOP!

WHAT DO YOU THINK, KHASBAH? I SAY THE GREAT ABIS MAL IS TAKING MORE THAN HIS FAIR SHARE!

PERHAPS WE SHOULD RELIEVE HIM OF-- WHAZZAT?!

GHOSTS! BAH! I'LL SOON SEE WHO'S THE MONKEY AROUND--

...HERE!

OOKABOLLAPONGA?

PUT HIM DOWN, ABIS MAL!

EH? WHO ARE YOU?!

MY *FRIENDS* CALL ME AL! YOU CAN CALL ME ALADDIN.

⇥GRR!⇤ GET HIM!

YIKES! END OF THE LINE--

-:WHOOF!- NICE CATCH, *CARPET!* NOT A *SECOND* TOO SOON!

THOSE PUNKS KNOW *WORDS* WILL NEVER HURT ME...SO THEY'RE *CUTTING* RIGHT TO THE *STICKS* AND *STONES!*

I THINK *I'LL* CUT TO THE *CHASE!* PARDON *ME!*

A FLYIN' *CARPET?!* HE'S GOT A *FLYIN'* CARPET!

RRRRUUUMMMBLE!

ZOW!

A *FAST* FLYING CARPET, TOO! NEXT STOP--AGRABAH!

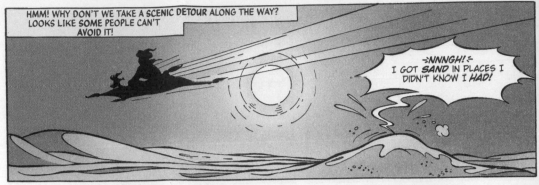

...YOU'D STILL BE IN A *CAGE* IN THE *BAZAAR!*

-=GRR!=-
YEAH, *RIGHT!* YOU'RE NOTHING WITHOUT ME, PAL...

IMAGINE, IAGO! THAT *STREET RAT* ALADDIN AND THAT *PRIG* PRINCESS JASMINE! THEY TURNED ME INTO A *GENIE* AND THOUGHT THEY WERE *RID* OF ME!

YEAH, YEAH! I'M STARTIN' TO WISH *I* WAS!

WHO COMES UP WITH ALL OUR GOOD IDEAS? *ME!* WHO DOES ALL THE WORK? *ME!*

SO WHY DON'T I *LOOK OUT* FOR ME...FOR A *CHANGE?*

IAGO! ARE YOU *CHANGING DIRECTION?*

YOU MIGHT SAY THAT! LOOK OUT BELOW!

ARRIVADERCI! C'EST LA VIE!

AT THAT MOMENT... IN A SLIGHTLY MORE WELCOMING PLACE!

HOME!

WE'RE NOT THE ONES WHO *NEED* THIS MONEY, ABU!

BUT I CAN THINK OF A *FEW* POOR PEOPLE WHO *DO*!

-:HEH!:- DON'T WORRY! GIMME THAT...I'M NOT THROWING AWAY *EVERYTHING*!

UH-UH?

NOPE! *THIS* IS FOR *JASMINE*, LI'L BUDDY! WHATCHA SAY? CHIMP GOT YOUR TONGUE?

ROWR!

AW, DON'T BE LIKE THAAAA--*YIPE!*

450

MEANWHILE! IAGO FINALLY MAKES IT BACK INTO THE CITY...FEELING VERY PLEASED WITH HIMSELF!

I COVER MY *OWN* TAIL NOW!

SEEMS LIKE ONLY YESTERDAY JAFAR WAS RUNNIN' AGRABAH! BUT THEN HE HAD TO GO AND *MESS THINGS UP!* I GOTTA GET *BACK* INTO THE PALACE--

WELL, MY DEAR ABU! SHALL WE SEE WHAT THE *COMMON* PEOPLE ARE DOING TODAY? ÷HEH!÷ WE HAVE TIME FOR A STROLL BEFORE OUR AUDIENCE WITH THE SULTAN!

THE *STREET RAT* IS LIVING IN THE *PALACE* NOW? ÷AWK!÷ THAT DOES IT! ALL REPORTS ARE IN!

WITH HIM IN, *I'LL* OUT! LIFE IS NOW OFFICIALLY UNFAIR!

NO--WAIT! WAIT A SECOND! THIS IS *PERFECT!* THAT KID IS MY TICKET BACK INTO POWER!

I'LL JUST GET HIM ON MY *SIDE*...WITH A LITTLE *SYMPATHY* ACT!

GUARD! IT IS THAT *THIEF*, ABIS MAL!

!

UH...*THANKS* FOR YOUR HELP. YOU *SAVED* ME.

I *DID?!* I MEAN, *SURE!* WANNA *ADOPT* ME? HUH? *HUH?*

WE'LL *SEE* ABOUT THAT. BUT DEFINITELY OWE YOU.

HEY! EASY ON THE *FEATHERS!*

SOON, AT THE PALACE...

DON'T WORRY! I'LL SEE THAT THE SULTAN GIVES YOU A *FAIR* HEARING.

WHAT?! THE *SULTAN?!* BUT-BUT-BUT--

AND JASMINE...WELL, FOR NOW LET'S KEEP YOU OUT OF HER SIGHT!

ER...*HI*, PRINCESS! SHAME ABOUT THAT *STAIN* ABU GOT ON THE BRAND-NEW *VEST* YOU GAVE HIM!

THAT'S FUNNY! I DON'T *SEE* A STAIN...

N-NO PROBLEM, THEN! OFF TO *DINNER!*

IS SOMETHING *WRONG?* YOU SEEM *NERVOUS.*

YOU AREN'T *HIDING* ANYTHING FROM ME, ARE YOU? ANY MORE... *SECRETS?*

ER...OF *COURSE* NOT, PRINCESS! ->GULP!<- I ALMOST *LOST* YOU ONCE THAT WAY. I'LL *NEVER* MAKE THAT MISTAKE--

...*AGAIN!* WHAT THE--

SHA BOOEY!

YEE-HAH! HE'S *BIG* AND HE'S *BLUE*...AND HE'S *BACK!*

I'VE TRAVELLED EAST AND WEST! BUT NOW THAT I'M *HOME* AGAIN, IT'S CLEAR...ALL I EVER *WANTED* SEEMS TO BE *RIGHT HERE!*

GENIE! YOU CAME *BACK!*

->OOH! AAH! OOH!<- WATCH THE *SUNBURN!*

DIDJA *MISS* ME? BE HONEST! HANG ON, I GOT SOUVENIRS FOR EVERYBODY!

NOW FOLLOW THE *RHYMING VERSE!* IN MEXI-CO, THEY WEAR A SOM-BRER-O...

A PARASOL THEY CARRY DOWN IN TOKY-O!

THE POLO CAP IN MOSCOW, IT IS TOO BIG, YES? SHOULD BE *"NO,"* BUT IN *RUSSIA,* VERSE RHYMES YOU!!

IT'S A *SMALL WORLD* AFTER ALL! BUT *AGRABAH* HAS SOMETHING THAT *NO* OTHER PLACE IN THE WORLD HAS...

YOU GUYS! THERE'S *NOTHING* IN THE WORLD QUITE LIKE A *FRIEND!*

GENIE, I'D BE HONORED IF YOU'D JOIN US FOR DINNER. AND *CATCH US UP!* HOW DOES IT FEEL TO BE *FREE?*

MY *POWERS* AREN'T AS STRONG. BUT I CAN STILL MONKEY AROUND WITH ABU!

UH...SOUNDS LIKE FUN, GENIE! BUT ABU'S NOT GONNA BE EATING WITH US! HE'S GOT A *JOB* TO DO.

OOK?!

REMEMBER? YOU HAFTA *GUARD IAGO!*

~GROAN!~

OUT IN THE DESERT, LATER IN THE EVENING! SEE THE DESERT ROBBERS, DREAMING OF THEIR LOAD...

THAT *STINKING* ALADDIN! FIRST CHANCE I GET, I'LL SLICE HIM IN HALF!

COME WASH UP, MEN! IT'S BAD ENOUGH I HAVE TO *LOOK* AT YA WITHOUT HAVIN' TO *SMELL* YA!

THAT *STINKING* ABIS MAL! FIRST CHANCE WE GET, LET'S SLICE HIM IN HALF!

OOH! WHAT IS *THIS*?

A *LAMP!* WELL! *IT* MIGHT BE WORTH...

GASP!

...A FEW *SHEKELS* ONCE IT'S CLEANED UP!

GUH?

POOF!

I AM FREE! FREE TO EXACT VENGEANCE UPON HE WHO IMPRISONED ME!

EXCEPT...I'M *BOUND* BY THE *GENIE RULES!* SO I *CAN'T* KILL ALADDIN UNLESS MY *MASTER ARRANGES* IT!

MASTER? →GLUB! BLUB!←

→HMM!← I'M *TOO MUCH* FOR HIS LIMITED MIND!

HOW'S *THIS*, FOOL? LESS *OVERWHELMING?*

Y-YOU'RE...A *GENIE?*

YOU ARE *ASTONISHINGLY* PERCEPTIVE.

UM →AHEM!← IF YOU'RE A *GENIE*, THEN DON'T I GET *WISHES?*

YES. *THREE* WISHES...

THAT *IS* A MINOR FORMALITY. BUT FIRST *I* MUST GO TO *AGRABAH!* TAKE THE LAMP THERE FOR ME!

MAYBE I WILL!

WHAT? YOU *DARE* TALK BACK?

WHY *NOT?* YOU *NEED* ME! I'LL TAKE YOU TO AGRABAH, BUT *FIRST* I WANT MY *WISHES!*

HMM...THIS *BLATHERSKITE* KNOWS *TOO MUCH* ABOUT GENIES! I CAN'T DISOBEY HIM. I'M *STUCK!*

YOU... SHALL HAVE YOUR WISHES! ~SIGH!~

GOOD! *FIRST*, I WISH FOR THE LEGENDARY SUNKEN TREASURE SHIP OF *COEUR DU MER!*

YOUR WISH IS MY COMMAND.

POOF!

THOUGH YOU'LL WANT TO LEARN TO WISH *WISELY!*

GLUB!

BLUB!

BLOOG

NOM

GLOM

POOR, SWEET BABY! PERHAPS YOU *WISH* ME TO RETURN YOU TO THE *DESERT?*

YSS

BLUB

BLUB!

THAT'S *TWO* WISHES! TAKE YOUR *TIME* WITH THE THIRD...

...OR YOU WILL *WISH* YOU HAD NEVER BEEN *BORN!*

OF COURSE, YOU *COULD* COOPERATE! HELP ME GET *REVENGE* ON A STREET RAT NAMED *ALADDIN!*

ALADDIN?! I WANT REVENGE ON HIM, *TOO!*

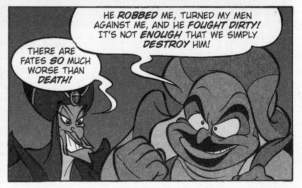

HE *ROBBED* ME, TURNED MY MEN AGAINST ME, AND HE *FOUGHT DIRTY!* IT'S NOT *ENOUGH* THAT WE SIMPLY *DESTROY* HIM!

THERE ARE FATES *SO* MUCH WORSE THAN *DEATH!*

BACK AT THE PALACE!

OKAY! PREPARE YOURSELVES FOR A REAL CULINARY *TREAT!*

HI-YAH! HI-YAH!

CHOP-CHOPPITY-CHOP!

WHOOPSIE!

MOST AMUSING!

~HA!~ AMUSING... *RIGHT!*

ABSOLUTELY *DELIGHTFUL!* I'M *SO* GLAD YOU'RE BACK!

EXCUSE ME WHILE I PULL MYSELF TOGETHER!

NOW, TO BUSINESS! ALADDIN, YOU HAVE PROVEN TO BE A MAN OF *STRONG MORAL CHARACTER.*

THAT IS WHY I'VE DECIDED TO MAKE *YOU* MY NEW *ROYAL VIZIER!*

ME? *REALLY?!*

ISN'T IT *WONDERFUL?*

WOW! ROYAL VIZIER! LET'S GET THIS PARTY *STARTED!*

ALADDIN WOULD LIKE TO *THANK* THE ACADEMY FOR THIS *GREAT* HONOR! SOLID BRASS TROPHY HERE, AL! NO DIME STORE PHONY!

APPLAUSE! *PLEASE!* I'M NOT *HEARING* THE YAY!

AND *THIS* IS--?

SIGN-UP SHEET FOR THE *ROYAL TRUST FUND!* 'CAUSE THE *VIZIER'S* THE MOST *TRUSTED* ADVISOR!

THAT'S A *GIANT LEAP* FOR A STREET RAT!

YOU *WANT* 'EM? WE *GOT* 'EM! *ROYAL VIZIER T-SHIRTS*, AL BABY!

AW, YOU *PREFER* YOUR PRINCELY ROBE? SPOILSPORT!

POOF!

IT *IS* A GREAT HONOR, ALADDIN!

SENSIBLE ONE, TOO! HE'S *BOUND* TO BE BETTER THAN THAT *JAFAR* CHARACTER!

AND *IAGO?* THAT BIRD WAS *MEAN!*

"SULTAN WANT A CRACKER! SULTAN WANT A CRACKER!"

THOSE *VILLAINS!*

UH...GENIE? IT'S *FUNNY* YOU SHOULD *MENTION* IAGO--

I *TRUST* YOU CAN EXPLAIN? HE *SERVED* MY GREATEST *ENEMY!*

IAGO WAS...UH, UNDER JAFAR'S *SPELL!* REMEMBER THE SNAKE-STAFF?

IAGO'S NOT *ALL* THAT *BAD!*

I DON'T BELIEVE IT!

EVEN *I* DON'T BELIEVE IT! "NOT ALL THAT BAD?" SHOULDA STUCK WITH THE SNAKE-STAFF DEFENSE!

~HARRUMPH!~ IF YOU WANT THIS TRAITOROUS BIRD FREE, SO *BE* IT! BUT THEN YOU'LL TAKE *FULL RESPONSIBILITY* FOR HIM! NO MORE *SECRET HIDING PLACES!*

SECRETS! I THOUGHT YOU HAD *CHANGED,* ALADDIN.

FREE! *FREE!* HANDS OFF THE MERCHANDISE, TUBBY!

BAH! IF THE BIRD MAKES *ONE* WRONG MOVE, *YOU* SHALL BE THE ONE I *PLUCK,* BOY!

UH...THAT *COULDA* GONE WORSE. JASMINE'S JUST A *LITTLE* STEAMED--

TRY *ON FIRE.* SOME GRAND VIZIER *I'M* GONNA MAKE!

THAT KID *SAVED MY LIFE!* NOBODY'S *EVER* LOOKED OUT FOR ME BEFORE! IT'S LIKE I...I *OWE* HIM.

NEXT DAY!

SO YOU'RE *SURE* I SHOULD GIVE HIM A CHANCE?

I CAN'T *EXPLAIN* IT, JASMINE! BUT *I* THINK WE CAN *TRUST* IAGO.

UH, I-I WAS JUST *THINKING*...

MAYBE IT'S TIME YOU *PATCHED THINGS UP* WITH THE SULTAN! UH-- GIVE HIM A *GIFT!* HE MIGHT ENJOY...

...UH, A NICE, SCENIC--ER, *MAGIC CARPET RIDE?*

HMM...THAT'S A GOOD IDEA!

AND *I'LL* BRING *GENIE!*

NO! NO, NO! UM...I MEAN, GENIE'S TOO *FLASHY!* HE'S TOO *LOUD!* YOU'D NEVER GET A *WORD* IN!

GOOD POINT, IAGO! YOU NEED SOME *QUIET* TIME WITH FATHER. LET HIM GET TO *KNOW* YOU!

YEAH! AND *I*--

...I HAVE THE *PERFECT SPOT!*

GREAT! C'MON, LET'S GET THE SULTAN!

QUITE A WAYS FROM THE PALACE...

THAT'S THE SPOT--

MY, *MY!* HEE-HEE-HEE!

HA-HA-HA! OH, WHAT *FUN!*

THIS WAS A GREAT IDEA, IAGO! THANKS!

DON'T THANK ME. *REALLY.*

SOMETHING YOU WANTED TO *TALK* ABOUT, ALADDIN?

YEAH! SULTAN, LOOK...

I'M *SORRY* FOR NOT TELLING YOU ABOUT IAGO. I *GUESS* I SAW SOME *GOOD* IN HIM!

REALLY?

JUST LIKE *YOU* SAW SOME GOOD IN A *STREET RAT--*

EH?

LOOK, THEY'RE TRAPPED!

WHOA!

WHEN THEY STOP, WE'LL-- HUH?!

ABIS MAL KNOWS MAGIC?!

GOTTA SAVE THE SULTAN!

BUT THEN...

RUMBLE!

SPLOOF!

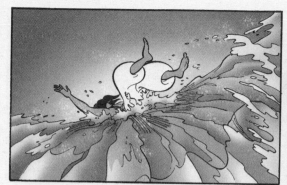

YEE-HEE-HEE-HEEEE! *YES*--

?!

NO! TOO *SOON,* ABIS MAL!

IT IS NOT YET *TIME* FOR THE BOY TO MEET HIS END!

ARE YOU *NUTS?!*

REMEMBER THE *PLAN.*

SOON, OUR *REVENGE* WILL BE COMPLETE AND *YOU* SHALL HAVE YOUR... *THIRD WISH...*

NOT SOON ENOUGH...

JAFAR, YOU FIEND! I SHOULD HAVE KNOWN THIS WAS YOUR TREACHERY!

ONE OF MY SNEAKIER PLANS, IT'S TRUE!

BUT I COULDN'T HAVE DONE IT WITHOUT IAGO!

~ULP!~ I-I PLAYED A MINOR ROLE, REALLY!

OOOH! WHEN ALADDIN RETURNS...

~TUT~ I THINK WE HAVE AMPLE TIME TO PREPARE FOR HIS ARRIVAL!

COME TO PAPA...

YES...ALADDIN WILL BE AWHILE TRAVERSING THE SHIFTING SANDS.

HEY! I COULDA WORN THAT HAT!

SLASH!

MY DEAR ABIS MAL! THIS HAT AND THIS DAGGER ARE EXACTLY WHAT WE NEED TO SEAL ALADDIN'S DOOM!

MUCH, MUCH LATER! HOME IS THE HERO...

RASOUL! THE SULTAN'S BEEN--

SEIZE HIM!

...AND YOU *SURVIVED* THE WATERFALL WITHOUT A *SCRATCH!* HOW VERY *CONVENIENT!*

IT'S THE *TRUTH!* WHY WON'T YOU *BELIEVE* ME?

BECAUSE WE *KNOW* YOU'RE LYING!

I FOUND *THIS* IN YOUR ROOM! MY FATHER'S TURBAN...*SLASHED!* I THOUGHT YOU *LOVED* ME, BUT YOU ONLY LOVE *POWER!*

I NEVER WANTED--

HE SHALL DIE AT DAWN.

YOU'RE IN *MY* HANDS NOW, STREET RAT!

HEH-HEH-HEH!

OH, YOU SHOULD HAVE SEEN THE *LOOK* ON ALADDIN'S FACE...

...WHEN *PRINCESS JASMINE* ARRESTED HIM...

...AND *SENTENCED* HIM TO *DEATH!*

MWAHAHA!

JAFAR! IAGO, I SWEAR...

...ONE DAY YOU WILL *PAY* FOR THIS!

SUNRISE!

JASMINE! I *KNEW* YOU WOULDN'T GO THROUGH WITH--

I JUST WANTED TO SAY *GOODBYE*...

...STREET RAT!

"JAFAR?! IT'S JAFAR?"

WHAT ARE YOU DOING *NOW*, YOU *DOUBLE-CROSSER*?

WHAT'S IT *LOOK* LIKE? TRYIN' TO *FREE* THE CHUMP GENIE...

...SO HE CAN *SAVE* YOUR CHUMP... ...BOY-FRIEND!

⇥AWWK!⇤

EEEK!

HAR HAR

SWISH

CHONK!

GENIE!

THAT *NO-HEAD* LOOK IS JUST NOT *YOU!*

AND *EVERYBODY'S* SAFE 'N' SOUND!

IAGO! YOU *SET ME UP!* YOU'RE NOTHING BUT A--

ALADDIN, HE *RESCUED* US. HE DIDN'T *HAVE* TO, BUT HE DID!

THERE'S NO TELLING *WHAT* JAFAR WILL DO TO AGRABAH! WE HAVE A *RESPONSIBILITY*...

"...AND IF WE DESTROY THE LAMP, WE'LL DESTROY JAFAR!"

YOUR *THIRD WISH*, ABIS MAL! YOU WILL NOW WISH ME *FREE* OF THAT WRETCHED *LAMP!*

NO! *MY* WISH! YOU GOT YOUR REVENGE! *MY* TURN!

BUT WHY *WASTE* A *WISH?* YOU WANT MORE *TREASURE?*

POOF!

...IT'S YOURS!

NOW, PERHAPS YOU'D CARE TO GRANT MY FREEDOM!

OH, YEAH...RIGHT! I HEREBY *WISH* FOR *JAFAR* TO BE--

?!?

GLOM

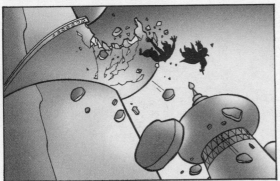

NOOOOOO!

FWOOF

RUMBLE!

IAGO! BUT...BUT I THOUGHT...

...A GENIE COULDN'T KILL ANYONE...

YOU'D BE SURPRISED WHAT YOU CAN LIVE THROUGH.

AND SO THE BIRD LIVED HAPPILY EVER AFTER!

OOT-GREET!

The End

HER HIGHNESS, THE PRINCESS OF...

GLOWERHAVEN?

GREETINGS, YOUR HIGHNESS.

AND GREETINGS TO *YOU*, YOUR... *uh*... YOUR HIGHNESS. WOULD YOU, *uh*... CARE TO DANCE?

I'D LOVE TO.

WHOOAAAH!

WOOOSH!

YOU *SEE*? I *KNEW* THAT ERIC WOULD GET ALONG SPLENDIDLY WITH HER HIGHNESS.

IF YOU ASK *ME*, HER HIGHNESS IS PRESENTING A LITTLE PROBLEM. LIKE... MAYBE TOO *MUCH* HIGHNESS.

CARLOTTA! I TAKE IT *BACK*! A SHRIMP WOULD LOOK REALLY *GOOD* ABOUT NOW!

Disney's MULAN the MIGHTY DRAGON

LEGEND SAYS, IF THE VILLAGERS BEHOLD A POWERFUL DRAGON THEY WILL HAVE GOOD FORTUNE AT HARVEST TIME. THAT'S WHY I'VE SUMMONED YOU, MUSHU.

WELL, ALL RIGHT!

ONE POWERFUL DRAGON REPORTING FOR DUTY! POINT ME TOWARD THAT LUCKY VILLAGE!

UH, NO MUSHU....

YOU HAVE NOT EARNED THE STATUS OF A GUARDIAN DRAGON, MUSHU.

BEHOLD! MUSHU, THE SWEET-AND-SOUR SHRIMP!

HA, HA, HA!

YOUR TASK IS TO BANG THE GONG AND AWAKEN THE STONE DRAGON.

B-BUT...

BANG THE GONG! THAT'S ALL I *EVER* DO IS BANG THE GONG!

OF COURSE, FIRST I HAVE TO *FIND* THE GONG. I KNOW I LEFT IT HERE SOMEPLACE.

GUESS THIS WHISTLE WILL HAVE TO DO.

YO, ROCKY! RISE AND SHINE!

♪ TWEEE! TWEEE! ♫

LOOKS LIKE NOBODY'S HOME.

NOW WHAT AM I GONNA DO?

I'VE GOTTA COME UP WITH A BIG, POWERFUL DRAGON SOMEHOW.

HOLD STILL, MULAN. YOU MUST LOOK PERFECT WHEN WE TAKE YOU TO SEE THE MATCHMAKER.

MULAN?

HEY! THAT GIVES ME AN IDEA!

I DIDN'T EVEN RECOGNIZE HER. SHE LOOKS ALL GROWN-UP!

HEY! TAXI!

TAKE ME TO THE VILLAGE AND *STEP ON IT!*

THE ANCESTORS THINK I'M JUST A SHRIMP, BUT I'LL SHOW 'EM!

I'VE GOT A PLAN.

ALL IT TAKES TO BE A BIG, POWERFUL DRAGON IS TO *LOOK* AND *ACT* LIKE A BIG, POWERFUL DRAGON!

HERE WE ARE, CABBIE! PULL OVER!

THIS IS WHERE THEY STORE EVERYTHING FOR FESTIVALS, PARADES AND SPECIAL OCCASIONS!

AND HERE'S WHAT I'M LOOKING FOR, ONE PAPER DRAGON SUIT, SIZE *EXTRA LARGE!*

OOF! I'M NOT GOING TO FOOL ANYBODY DRAGGING THIS DRAGON ALONG THE GROUND!

Aha! STILTS! THIS'LL GIVE ME THE STATURE I SO *RICHLY* DESERVE!

FEE-FI-FO-FUM! LOOK AT MUSHU NOW, HERE I COME!

WHAT ARE YOU LAUGHING AT? THIS IS ALL PART OF MY MASTER PLAN TO WAKE THE VILLAGERS AND GET THEIR ATTENTION!

BEHOLD, PEOPLE! I AM THE MIGHTY MUSHU! HERE TO BRING YOU GOOD FORTUNE!

UH, HELLO? MAY I HAVE YOUR ATTENTION PLEASE?

I SUPPOSE YOU HAVE A BETTER IDEA?!!

LATER THAT NIGHT.

WAKE UP, BLOCKHEAD! IF YOU WANT THIS POWERFUL DRAGON JOB YOU CAN HAVE IT!

CLANK, CLANK, CLANK!

END

Once Upon a Time in a FARAWAY LAND, a young PRINCE LIVED IN A SHINING CASTLE.

Disney's *Beauty AND THE BEAST*

KJN002-1

Although he had everything his heart desired, the Prince was spoiled, selfish and unkind.

One winter's night, an old beggar woman came to the castle and offered him a single rose in return for shelter from the bitter cold.

Repulsed by her haggard appearance, the Prince sneered at the gift and turned the old woman away.

But she warned him not to be deceived by appearances -- for beauty is found within.

And when he dismissed her again, the old woman's ugliness melted away to reveal...

...a beautiful enchantress!

The Prince tried to apologize, but it was too late -- for she had seen that there was no love in his heart.

As punishment, she transformed the Prince into a hideous Beast...

...and placed a powerful spell on the castle and all who lived there.

Ashamed of his monstrous form, the Beast concealed himself inside his castle with a Magic Mirror as his only window to the outside world.

The rose she had offered was truly an enchanted Rose which would bloom until his 21st year.

If he could learn to love another and earn her love in return by the time the last petal fell, then the spell would be broken.

If not -- he would be doomed to remain a Beast for all time.

As the years passed, he fell into despair and lost all hope...

...for who could ever learn to love a Beast?

And now, 10 years later...

ANOTHER BEAUTIFUL DAY!

ANOTHER TRIP INTO TOWN!

PAPA, DO YOU THINK I'M....ODD?

MY DAUGHTER? ODD? NOW WHERE WOULD YOU GET AN IDEA LIKE THAT?

THEN WHAT ARE WE WAITING FOR? I'LL HAVE THIS THING FIXED IN NO TIME!

I JUST DON'T FIT IN HERE. I WANT ADVENTURE--EXCITEMENT-- AND SOMEONE TO SHARE IT WITH!

WHAT ABOUT GASTON? HE'S A HANDSOME FELLA!

NO, THANKS!

WELL, DON'T YOU WORRY, 'CAUSE THIS INVENTION'S GOING TO BE THE START OF A WHOLE NEW LIFE FOR US!

LET'S GIVE HER ANOTHER TRY!

CHOONK!

IT WORKS, PAPA! YOUR WOOD CHOPPER WORKS!

CHOP! CHOP! CHOP!

AND SO...

GOODBYE! GOOD LUCK, PAPA!

GOODBYE, BELLE! TAKE CARE WHILE I'M GONE!

HOURS LATER...

WE SHOULD BE THERE BY NOW! MAYBE WE MISSED THE TURN...

HA-ROOOOO!

WOLVES!

NEEHRHRHR!

HA-ROOOOO!

PHILLIPE-- NOOO--!

SPLOOP!

HA-ROOOOO!

PHILLIPE!

COME BACK!

GRRRR!

HELP! SOMEBODY-- HEEELP!

A GATE! I'VE GOT TO GET INSIDE!

GRRRR!

'ALLO, MONSIEUR!

INCREDIBLE! HOW IS THIS ACCOMPLISHED? THESE AREN'T PUPPETS!

HMM...

SIR! SIR, PUT ME DOWN AT ONCE OR I WILL BE FORCED TO GIVE YOU A SOUND THRASHING!

WHY... WHY, YOU'RE ALIVE!

BUT OF COURSE!

AHH-CHOOO!

WHY, YOU ARE SOAKED TO THE BONE, MONSIEUR!

COME--WARM YOURSELF BY THE FIRE!

¡ sniff !¡ THANK YOU!

NO! LUMIERE, I FORBID IT! THE MASTER WILL BE FURIOUS IF HE FINDS HIM HERE!

NO NO NO-- NOT THE MASTER'S CHAIR!

ARP! ARP!

OH, NO-- NOT THE DOG!

SIT!

STAY!

WOULD YOU LIKE A SPOT OF TEA, SIR? IT'LL WARM YOU UP IN NO TIME!

NO-- NO TEA! NO TEA!!

WE'VE GOT TO GET HIM *OUT* OF HERE! YOU *KNOW* WHAT THE MASTER WILL *DO* IF HE--

CALM YOURSELF, COGSWORTH! THE MASTER WILL NEVER HAVE TO *KNOW!*

BUT--

THERE'S A *STRANGER* HERE!

M-MASTER-- ALLOW ME TO *EXPLAIN!*

THE GENTLEMAN WAS *LOST* IN THE *WOODS* AND--

WHAT ARE YOU *DOING* HERE?

YOU'RE NOT *WELCOME!*

PLEASE-- I MEANT NO HARM-- I JUST NEEDED A PLACE TO STAY!

I'LL GIVE YOU A PLACE TO *STAY!*

MEANWHILE, OUTSIDE BELLE'S COTTAGE...

I'D LIKE TO *THANK* YOU ALL FOR COMING TO MY *WEDDING!*

THIS IS *BELLE'S* LUCKY *DAY!*

BUT *FIRST,* I'D BETTER GO IN THERE AND *PROPOSE* TO THE GIRL! *HA HA!*

BOO-HOO!

NOW, LEFOU-- WHEN *BELLE* AND I COME OUT THAT *DOOR*--

I *KNOW,* I KNOW-- STRIKE UP THE BAND!

KNOCK KNOCK!

GASTON! WHAT A -- er-- PLEASANT SURPRISE!

ISN'T IT, THOUGH? I'M JUST *FULL* OF SURPRISES!

THIS IS THE DAY YOUR *DREAMS* COME *TRUE*, BELLE!

WHAT DO YOU KNOW ABOUT MY *DREAMS*, GASTON?

PLENTY!

PICTURE THIS -- A *RUSTIC* HUNTING LODGE... MY LATEST *KILL* ROASTING ON THE FIRE... SIX OR SEVEN *LITTLE ONES* PLAYING ON THE FLOOR WITH THE *DOGS*... AND MY LITTLE *WIFE*--

--MASSAGING MY *FEET*...

DO YOU KNOW *WHO* THAT LITTLE WIFE WILL *BE*?

YOU, BELLE!

GASTON-- I *REALLY* DON'T KNOW WHAT TO SAY!

SAY YOU'LL *MARRY* ME!

I'M VERY *SORRY*, GASTON, BUT... BUT...

...BUT *THANKS* FOR ASKING!

WHOOOA--!

SHE TURNED YA *DOWN*, HUH?

TURNED ME DOWN?! NONSENSE!

SHE'S JUST, UH.... PLAYING *HARD* TO GET!

I'LL HAVE BELLE FOR MY WIFE *ONE WAY* OR ANOTHER!

IS HE *GONE?*

BRAAAK!

CAN YOU *IMAGINE?* HE ASKED ME TO *MARRY* HIM! *ME*, THE WIFE OF THAT *BOORISH, BRAINLESS--*

NEERRHRHR!

PHILLIPE! WHAT ARE *YOU* DOING HERE?

WHERE'S *PAPA?!*

WHAT *HAPPENED?!* OH, WE HAVE TO *FIND* HIM!

PHILLIPE, YOU HAVE TO *TAKE* ME TO HIM!

AND SOON, DEEP WITHIN THE FOREST...

ALL RIGHT, CALM *DOWN*, PHILLIPE! WHICH WAY DO WE GO *NOW?*

WHERE IS THIS PLACE?

PHILLIPE-- THERE'S PAPA'S HAT!

COME ON-- WE'RE GOING INSIDE!

HELLO?

IS ANYONE HERE?

PAPA!

PAPA! IT'S BELLE!

COULDN'T KEEP QUIET, COULD WE? JUST HAD TO INVITE HIM TO STAY, DIDN'T WE?

I WAS TRYING TO BE HOSPITABLE!

PAPA!

HUH??

DID YOU SEE THAT? IT'S A GIRL!

I KNOW IT'S A GIRL!

DON'T YOU *SEE?* SHE'S THE *ONE!* SHE HAS COME TO BREAK THE *SPELL!*

NOW WAIT A *MINUTE!* LET'S NOT GET CARRIED AWAY!

ISN'T IT *WONDERFUL?* AFTER ALL THESE *YEARS!*

SHE'S COME FOR THAT POOR *FELLOW!* HE MUST BE HER *FATHER!*

THEN WE MUST *HELP* HER TO *FIND* HIM, NO?

AND SO...

IS IT *TRUE?* IS THERE A *GIRL* HERE?

YES, *INDEED!* BUT KEEP A *LID* ON IT! WE DON'T WANT THE WHOLE *HOUSE* IN AN *UPROAR!*

COGSWORTH, DOWN HERE *TOUTE DE SUITE!* WE CAN *LURE* HER TO HER *FATHER!*

ARF! ARF!

HELLO? WHO'S THERE?

BELLE? ⸨coff coff⸩ IS THAT *YOU?*

PAPA!!

HOW DID YOU *FIND* ME?

YOUR *HANDS* ARE LIKE *ICE!* WE HAVE TO GET YOU *OUT* OF HERE!

BELLE ⸨coff coff⸩ YOU MUST *LEAVE* THIS PLACE! I'VE NO TIME TO *EXPLAIN*--

THUMP!

⸨GASP!⸩

WHO -- WHO ARE YOU?

THE MASTER OF THIS CASTLE.

I'VE COME FOR MY FATHER. THERE MUST BE SOME MIS-UNDERSTANDING. PLEASE, LET HIM OUT. CAN'T YOU SEE HE'S SICK?

THEN HE SHOULDN'T HAVE TRESPASSED HERE.

BUT HE COULD DIE! I'LL DO ANYTHING, PLEASE!

THERE MUST BE SOME WAY I CAN CONVINCE YOU--

WAIT! TAKE ME INSTEAD!

YOU WOULD TAKE HIS PLACE?

BELLE, NO--!

IF I STAY, WOULD YOU LET HIM GO?

YES. BUT YOU MUST PROMISE TO STAY HERE FOREVER.

COME INTO THE LIGHT.

YOU HAVE MY WORD.

NO, BELLE! ≥coff coff≤

NO, I WON'T LET YOU DO THIS--!!

HERE'S YOUR ROOM.

IF YOU NEED ANYTHING, MY SERVANTS WILL ATTEND YOU.

INVITE HER TO DINNER!

YOU'LL, UH,... JOIN ME FOR DINNER.

THAT'S NOT A REQUEST.

MEANWHILE, AT THE VILLAGE TAVERN...

WHO DOES SHE THINK SHE IS? THAT GIRL HAS TANGLED WITH THE WRONG MAN!

NO ONE SAYS NO TO GASTON!

DARN RIGHT! EH-- MORE BEER?

FLUMP!

OH, WHAT FOR? NOTHING HELPS! I'M DISGRACED! I'VE BEEN PUBLICLY HUMILIATED!

IT'S MORE THAN I CAN BEAR...

GASTON-- YOU'VE GOT TO PULL YOURSELF *TOGETHER!* WHY, YOU'RE THE HERO OF THE *TOWN*, THE MAN OF THE *HOUR!*

OH, YEAH, RIGHT...

IT JUST *BREAKS* MY HEART TO SEE YOU SO DOWN IN THE DUMPS! *SMILE*, FOR HEAVEN'S SAKE!

THAAAT'S BETTER!

AFTER ALL, GASTON-- YOU'VE GOT A *REPUTATION* TO UPHOLD!

YOU'RE THE ULTIMATE *MANLY MAN*, GASTON! A SYMBOL OF *STRENGTH!* A PINNACLE OF *PROWESS!* A BULWARK OF *BRAWN!*

YOU *LOOK* THE BEST, EH? YOU *HUNT* THE BEST, EH? AND YOU *SPIT* THE BEST! HA HA!

WHY-- YOU'RE *RIGHT*, LEFOU! IT'S AS PLAIN AS THE *GIRLS* AT MY *FEET!*

DARN *RIGHT!*

LET'S ALL *HEAR* IT FOR *ME!*

HIP HIP-- HOORAY! HIP HIP-- HOORAY! HIP HIP--

WHILE AT THE BEAST'S CASTLE...

TRY TO BE *PATIENT*, SIR! THE GIRL HAS LOST HER *FATHER* AND HER *FREEDOM* ALL IN ONE *DAY!*

WHAT'S TAKING HER SO LONG? I *TOLD* HER TO COME DOWN FOR *DINNER!*

MASTER--HAVE YOU THOUGHT THAT PERHAPS THIS *GIRL* COULD BE THE ONE TO BREAK THE *SPELL?*

OF *COURSE* I HAVE! I'M NO *FOOL!*

GOOD! SO--YOU FALL IN LOVE WITH *HER*--SHE FALLS IN LOVE WITH *YOU* AND--*POOF!* THE SPELL IS *BROKEN!*

WE'LL BE *HUMAN* AGAIN BY *MIDNIGHT!*

IT'S NOT THAT *EASY*, LUMIERE! THESE THINGS TAKE *TIME!*

BUT THE *ROSE* HAS ALREADY BEGUN TO *WILT!*

IT'S NO USE. SHE'S SO *BEAUTIFUL*, AND I'M ...

...WELL, LOOK AT ME!

YOU MUST HELP HER SEE *PAST* ALL THAT!

I DON'T KNOW HOW!

IMPRESS HER WITH YOUR RAPIER *WIT!*

BUT BE *GENTLE!*

SHOWER HER WITH *COMPLIMENTS!*

BUT BE *SINCERE!*

AND *ABOVE ALL--*

--YOU MUST CONTROL YOUR TEMPER!

WAIT-- HERE SHE *IS!*

KA-CHK!

WELL--WHERE *IS* SHE?

WHO? OH, HA HA -- THE *GIRL!* YES, UM ... WELL, ACTUALLY, UH ... SHE'S IN THE *PROCESS OF...*

...*WELL,* CIRCUMSTANCES BEING WHAT THEY *ARE...*

...SHE'S *NOT* COMING!

YOUR *LORDSHIP!* YOUR *GRACE!* YOUR *EMINENCE!*

LET'S NOT BE *HASTY!*

I *THOUGHT* I TOLD YOU TO COME DOWN TO *DINNER!*

I'M *NOT* HUNGRY!

RAP RAP RAP!

YOU COME OUT OR I'LL BREAK DOWN THE *DOOR!*

MASTER, I COULD BE *WRONG* BUT--THAT MAY *NOT* BE THE BEST WAY TO WIN THE GIRL'S *AFFECTIONS!*

GENTLY-- *GENTLY!*

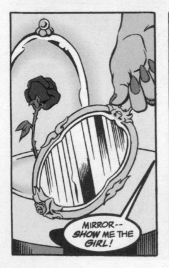

YOU ARE OUR HONORED *GUEST,* MADEMOISELLE! LET US PULL UP A CHAIR FOR YOU! RELAX AS THE *DINING ROOM* PROUDLY PRESENTS--

--YOUR *DINNER!*

TAKE A GLANCE AT THE *MENU,* CHERIE -- *SOUP DU JOUR!* HOT HORS D'OEUVRES!

WE LIVE ONLY TO *SERVE,* AND WE SERVE ONLY THE *BEST!*

YOU'RE *ALONE* HERE, AND *AFRAID,* BUT LOOK-- THE BANQUET IS *PREPARED!* EVERY DISH IN *PERFECT* TASTE AND SERVED WITH *FLAIR!*

AFTER ALL, MISS, THIS IS *FRANCE*--ALL THE DISHES *SING* AND *DANCE!* LET US SERVE YOU A *CULINARY CABARET!*

THERE'S *BEEF RAGOUT* AND *CHEESE SOUFFLE!* AND TRY THE *PIE* AND *PUDDING--*

--EN *FLAMBÉ!*

FWOOF!

YOU'RE A *GUEST*--A REAL *GUEST!* THANK HEAVENS I'VE HAD THE NAPKINS *FRESHLY PRESSED!*

YOU'LL WANT *TEA* WITH DESSERT, SO I MUST BREW THE WATER NICE AND *HOT!*

IT'S BEEN SO *LONG* SINCE WE'VE HAD A SOUL TO *WAIT* UPON-- TEN WHOLE *YEARS* WE'VE BEEN RUSTING!

THEN IN YOU WALK AND UPS-A-DAISY!

YOUR REQUEST IS OUR *COMMAND!* LET US SERVE AND *ENTERTAIN* YOU!

OUR ONLY AIM IS TO *PLEASE* YOU--

--OUR *GUEST!*

WOULD YOU LIKE A *TOUR,* MADEMOISELLE?

OH, YES!

WAIT! WAIT A SECOND! I'M *NOT* SURE THAT'S A *GOOD* IDEA, LUMIERE!

PERHAPS *YOU'D* LIKE TO TAKE ME! I'M SURE *YOU* KNOW *EVERYTHING* THERE IS TO KNOW ABOUT THE CASTLE!

WELL, ACTUALLY... I *DO!*

AND SO, MANY ROOMS AND CORRIDORS LATER...

NOW THEN-- IF I MAY DRAW YOUR ATTENTION TO THE *FLYING BUTTRESSES*--

THE *WEST WING*...

WAIT! DON'T GO!

PLEASE-- MADEMOISELLE!

SOON...

WE *MADE* IT, PHILLIPE! NOW WE JUST HAVE TO *FIND* OUR WAY *HOME*!

HA-OOOOOO!

OH, NO...

GRRRRR!

RUN, PHILLIPE-- *RUN!*

FASTER, PHILLIPE--

--RUN FASTER!!

GRRRR!

GRRRR! REERRRR!!

YIIEEE!

LATER, AT THE BEAST'S CASTLE...

HERE, NOW -- DON'T *DO* THAT!

JUST HOLD *STILL* AND LET ME --

ROAAAR!

GASP!

THAT HURTS!!

IF YOU'D HOLD *STILL*, IT WOULDN'T HURT AS *MUCH!*

IF YOU HADN'T RUN *AWAY*, THIS WOULDN'T HAVE *HAPPENED!*

IF YOU HADN'T *FRIGHTENED* ME, I WOULDN'T HAVE RUN *AWAY!*

WHILE AT BELLE'S COTTAGE...

IF NO ONE WILL *HELP* ME, THEN I'LL GO BACK *ALONE!*

LET'S SEE... MY *COMPASS...* OH, AND MY *MAPS...*

I DON'T CARE *WHAT* IT TAKES-- I'LL *FIND* THAT CASTLE AND *SOMEHOW--*

--I'LL GET BELLE *OUT* OF THERE!

AND ONLY MOMENTS LATER...

BELLE? MAURICE?

I'M *AFRAID* THERE'S NO ONE HOME!

THEY HAVE TO COME BACK *SOMETIME!* AND WHEN THEY *DO--*

--WE'LL BE *READY* FOR THEM!

AND THE NEXT MORNING...

I'VE NEVER *FELT* THIS WAY ABOUT ANYONE! I WANT TO *DO* SOMETHING FOR HER...

...BUT *WHAT?*

FLOWERS? CHOCOLATES?

NO NO--THIS IS NO *ORDINARY* GIRL! IT HAS TO BE SOMETHING VERY *SPECIAL...* SOMETHING THAT *SPARKS* HER INTEREST!

A-HAA-- I KNOW *JUST* THE THING!

AND SO TIME PASSES...

BUT WHO WOULD HAVE THOUGHT...

...WHO COULD HAVE GUESSED...

...WHAT MIGHT HAPPEN IN THAT TIME?

LATER...

TONIGHT IS THE NIGHT!

I'M NOT SURE I CAN DO THIS...

MASTER, YOU DON'T HAVE TIME TO BE TIMID! YOU CARE FOR THE GIRL, DON'T YOU?

MORE THAN ANYTHING!

WELL THEN -- YOU MUST TELL HER! YOU CAN DO IT!

I CAN DO IT!

THAT EVENING, THEY DANCE...

...AND AFTERWARDS...

BELLE, ARE YOU *HAPPY* HERE... WITH *ME?*

YES.

WHAT'S THE MATTER?

IF ONLY I COULD SEE MY *FATHER* AGAIN... JUST FOR A MOMENT. I *MISS* HIM SO MUCH.

THERE IS A *WAY.*

THAT MIRROR WILL SHOW YOU *ANYTHING* YOU WISH TO SEE.

I'D LIKE TO SEE MY *FATHER*, PLEASE.

WHAT DID YOU SAY?

I *RELEASE* YOU. YOU'RE NO LONGER MY *PRISONER.*

I'M--I'M *FREE?*

YES.

BELLE! ⸱coff coff⸱ BELLE--!

PAPA!

OH, HE'S *SICK--* HE MAY BE *DYING!* AND HE'S ALL *ALONE!*

THEN... YOU MUST GO TO HIM.

5

TAKE THE MIRROR WITH YOU. SO YOU'LL ALWAYS HAVE A WAY TO LOOK BACK... AND REMEMBER ME.

THANK YOU FOR UNDERSTANDING!

WELL, YOUR HIGHNESS -- I MUST SAY, EVERYTHING IS GOING SWIMMINGLY! I KNEW YOU HAD IT IN YOU!

I LET HER GO.

WHAT??? HOW COULD YOU DO THAT?!

I HAD TO.

WHY?!

BECAUSE I LOVE HER.

HE WHAT?

YES, I'M AFRAID IT'S TRUE.

SHE'S GOING AWAY?

BUT HE WAS SO CLOSE!

PHILLIPE, WE'VE GOT TO *FIND* HIM! THE MIRROR SAYS HE'S *THIS WAY!* HURRY!

PAPA!!

RUN, BELLE... RUN! IT SHOULD HAVE BEEN *ME*...

SOON, BACK AT THE COTTAGE...

IT SHOULD HAVE BEEN *ME*... *ME*...

IT'S ALL RIGHT, PAPA-- *I'M HOME!*

B-BELLE? BELLE!

YOU REALLY *HAVE* COME HOME! I THOUGHT I'D NEVER *SEE* YOU AGAIN!

BUT THE *BEAST*-- HOW DID YOU *ESCAPE?*

I *DIDN'T* ESCAPE--HE LET ME *GO!*

HE'S *DIFFERENT* NOW, PAPA! HE'S *CHANGED* SOMEHOW!

OH! A *STOWAWAY!*

HI!

BONK!

THUNK!

WHY, *HELLO* THERE, LITTLE FELLA! I DIDN'T THINK I'D LIKE TO SEE *YOU* AGAIN!

BELLE, WHY'D YOU GO AWAY? DON'T YOU *LIKE US* ANYMORE?

KNOCK KNOCK!

MAY I *HELP* YOU?

I'VE COME TO COLLECT YOUR *FATHER!*

MY FATHER--?

DON'T *WORRY*, MADEMOISELLE! WE'LL TAKE *GOOD CARE* OF HIM!

MY FATHER'S NOT *CRAZY!*

OH? HEY, MAURICE! TELL US *AGAIN*, OLD MAN-- JUST HOW BIG *WAS* THAT BEAST?

WELL, HE, UH, HE WAS *ENORMOUS!* I'D SAY *EIGHT*-- NO, MORE LIKE *TEN* FEET TALL!

HA HA HA! FOLKS, YOU DON'T GET MUCH CRAZIER THAN *THAT!*

POOR BELLE! IT'S A *SHAME* ABOUT YOUR FATHER!

YOU *KNOW* HE'S NOT CRAZY, GASTON!

HMM! I MAY BE ABLE TO CLEAR UP THIS LITTLE MISUNDERSTANDING IF--

--YOU MARRY ME!

ONE LITTLE *WORD*, BELLE! THAT'S *ALL* IT TAKES!

NEVER!

HAVE IT *YOUR WAY*, THEN!

WAIT! MY FATHER'S *NOT CRAZY*, AND I CAN *PROVE* IT!

MIRROR-- *SHOW* ME THE *BEAST*!

FLASH!

SEE? THERE HE *IS!* MY FATHER WAS TELLING THE *TRUTH!*

IS HE *DANGEROUS?*

SOON, AT THE BEAST'S CASTLE ...

SACRE BLEU-- INVADERS!

AND THEY HAVE THE MIRROR!

WE'VE GOT TO WARN THE MASTER!

TAKE WHATEVER *BOOTY* YOU CAN FIND, BUT REMEM-BER--THE BEAST IS *MINE!*

KILL THE BEAST!

BOOM!

KILL THE BEAST!

BOOM!

PARDON ME, MASTER--?

LEAVE ME IN *PEACE.*

BUT, SIR-- THE *CASTLE* IS UNDER *ATTACK!*

WELL...I MEAN, JUST A QUICK CHECK COULDN'T *HURT*. DADDY SUMMONED SO MANY PEOPLE TO THIS MEETING...HE WON'T NOTICE IF I'M NOT THERE *IMMEDIATELY*...

AND I CAN *ALWAYS* FIND OUT WHAT I MISSED. JUST SOME SORT OF OFFICIAL ANNOUNCEMENT OR SOMETHING, I BET.

AND AFTER ALL, IF SOMEONE IS *REALLY* IN TROUBLE, WHAT KIND OF PRINCESS WOULD I BE IF I IGNORED TH--

WELL, NOW, *THAT'S* WEIRD...

THERE'S NOBODY HERE. BUT I WAS *SURE* I HEARD CRYING.

THAT'S... *sniff*... *THAT'S* ALL RIGHT...

I WOULDN'T EXPECT YOU TO... *sniff*... NOTICE ME...

AFTER ALL...I WOULDN'T EXPECT AN...IMPORTANT *sniff* PERSON LIKE *YOU* TO *nuh*..NOTICE...

A NOBODY LIKE ME!!

WAAAAAHHHH!!!

OH, NOW, PLEASE, HONEY! DON'T CRY! EVERYTHING'S GOING TO BE ALL RIGHT!

I'M SORRY I DIDN'T SEE YOU AT FIRST. IT'S JUST THAT YOU'RE...

...SO LITTLE. I KNOW. I'M JUST A LITTLE GUPPY AND NOBODY CARES ABOUT ME.

NOW THAT'S NOT TRUE! I CARE ABOUT YOU. WHAT'S YOUR NAME?

GUINEVERE. GUINEVERE COREY GUPPY.

MY! SUCH AN IMPORTANT NAME!

MY FRIENDS CALL ME JENNY... IF I HAD FRIENDS...

WOULD YOU MIND IF I CALLED YOU JENNY?

YOU MEAN...YOU WANT TO BE MY FRIEND? ME BE WITH FRIENDS WITH PRINCESS ARIEL?

OF COURSE. BUT...YOU HAVE TO PROMISE ME THAT YOU'LL TELL ME WHAT'S REALLY BOTHERING YOU. THAT WAY YOU WERE CRYING SOUNDS JUST LIKE THE WAY ONE OF MY SISTERS CRIES WHEN SHE'S HEARTBROKEN OVER SOME MERMAN...

YOU'RE SO SMART, PRINCESS. THERE'S SOMEONE WHO I'M JUST CRAZY ABOUT...

AND HE CAN'T SEE ME FOR KELP. HE JUST TELLS ME TO GO AWAY AND STOP BOTHER- ING HIM.

"SILLY, LITTLE GUPPY" HE CALLS ME.

OH, REALLY? WELL MAYBE I SHOULD JUST HAVE A *TALK* WITH HIM. IF HE'S MAKING YOU SO UNHAPPY, HE SHOULD *KNOW* ABOUT IT.

WHAT'S HIS NAME?

FLOUNDER.

FLOUNDER! MY FRIEND FLOUNDER?

HE'S...YOUR FRIEND? YOU ACTUALLY *KNOW* HIM?

WHY, *SURE!* DON'T WORRY, JENNY. ONCE I LET FLOUNDER KNOW HOW YOU FEEL ABOUT HIM, YOUR PROBLEMS ARE *OVER.*

THIS IS SO WONDERFUL OF YOU TO TAKE TIME FROM YOUR IMPORTANT PRINCESSLY DUTIES...

OH, I'M SURE THERE WASN'T ANYTHING "PRINCESSLY" HAP-PENING *TODAY* THAT'S *REMOTELY* AS IMPOR-TANT AS HELPING A LOVELORN FRIEND.

MY PEOPLE... THERE IS *GRAVE* DANGER.

547

THERE HAVE BEEN SIGHTINGS THAT *SCARFACE* IS APPROACHING THE OUTER BOUNDARIES OF THE REALM.

SCARFACE, FATHER? THAT MONSTROUS KILLER *SHARK*? BUT HE HASN'T BEEN SEEN IN THESE PARTS FOR *AGES*.

THAT'S *CORRECT*, MY DEAR. BUT HE HAS RETURNED.

DAT BIG *BULLY*! TINKING HE CAN GO WHERE HE WANT AND DO WHAT HE WANT. YOU SHOULD JUST GIVE HIM WHAT-FOR, YOUR MAJESTY, AND HAVE *DONE* WID HIM!

AS MUCH AS I WOULD *LIKE* TO, SEBASTIAN...

...I CANNOT SIMPLY GO ABOUT ELIMINATING ALL THE DENIZENS OF THE UNDERSEA WORLD WHOM I DON'T LIKE. SCARFACE *IS* VICIOUS, BUT HE'S A *SHARK*. IT'S HIS *NATURE*, AND YOU DON'T OBLITERATE SOMEONE FOR BEING TRUE TO HIS NATURE.

IF HE ATTACKED THE CITY DIRECTLY, THAT WOULD BE *ANOTHER* MATTER...BUT HE'S TOO SMART, AND TOO WARY OF *ME*, TO DO THAT. SO INSTEAD I ALERT MY PEOPLE TO STAY CLOSE TO HOME UNTIL THE DANGER PASSES.

YES, YOUR MAJESTY.

THAT GOES FOR *ALL* OF YOU! BE EXTREMELY CAUTIOUS UNTIL I TELL YOU IT'S SAFE TO RESUME NORMAL ACTIVITIES. THAT'S ALL.

YES, SIR.

YES, YOUR MAJESTY.

FATHER? I DIDN'T SEE *ARIEL* HERE.

BLAST! JUST ONCE I'D LIKE TO SEE THAT GIRL WHERE SHE'S *SUPPOSED* TO BE, WHEN SHE'S SUPPOSED TO BE THERE.

AQUATA, ORGANIZE A SMALL SEARCH PARTY. SEND PEOPLE OUT IN ALL DIRECTIONS.

ALL DIRECTIONS.

THIS ISN'T JUST FOR ARIEL. I WANT TO MAKE SURE ALL CREATURES, GREAT AND SMALL, ARE ALERTED TO THE DANGER. BUT AS SOON AS ARIEL IS FOUND, BRING HER *HERE*.

STRAIGHT BACK HERE.

I HAVE A FEW WORDS FOR THAT GIRL.

A FEW CHOICE WORDS, *DAT* IS FOR SURE.

AND YOU GET OUT THERE AND LOOK FOR HER TOO, SEBASTIAN.

YES, I BETTER GET MYSELF OUT DERE AND FIND DAT...

MUH... ME?

BUT...BUT YOUR MAJESTY... DERE IS DAT SHARK COMING OUR WAY. MAYBE IT WOULD BE *BETTER* IF...

ARE YOU QUESTIONING MY *ORDER*, SEBASTIAN?

ME?

YOU.

NO!

GOOD.

WHY DO DESE TINGS HAPPEN TO ME? WHAT DID I DO TO DESERVE DIS? DA GREATEST MUSICAL MIND IN DA SEVEN SEAS, AND I'M OFF LOOKING FOR DAT GIRL. RIGHT NOW SHE'S IN MORE DANGER FROM *ME* DEN DAT SHARK, DAT'S FOR SURE.

FANTAIL! OVER HERE! FLIP IT *HERE!*

GO DEEP, FLOUNDER! GO *DEEP!*

uh, FANTAIL... AREN'T WE *ALL* DEEP? I MEAN, WE'RE UNDERWATER AND EVERYTHING...

OH, FOR TRITON'S SAKE, SNORKEL!

TOSS IT HERE! TOSS IT HERE! *I* GOT IT!

FLOUNDER... THERE'S SOMEONE WHO WANTS TO TALK TO YOU...

AND I THINK YOU SHOULD LISTEN TO WHAT SHE HAS TO SAY.

JENNY! WHAT ARE *YOU* DOING HERE!? I TOLD YOU TO LEAVE ME AL--

HIIII, FLOUNDER.

FLOUNDER! LOOK--

WONK!

OH, FLOUNDER, I'M *SORRY!*

FLOUNDER! OH, IT'S ALL *MY* FAULT! YOU HURT YOURSELF! ARE YOU ALL RIGHT? WHAT CAN I DO TO *HELP?!*

OH! OH! OOOOOH, FLOUNDER, LET US HEEELLLLP YOU!

TELL US WHERE IT HURTS AND WE'LL *KISS* IT AND MAKE IT ALLLLLL BETTER!

HAAHA HA HAWWWW HAWW!

♪ FLOUNDER AND JENNY, FLOATING IN THE SEA, K-I-S-S-I-N-G...♪

SEE WHAT YOU GUYS *DID*!! IT'LL TAKE ME *FOREVER* TO LIVE THIS DOWN!

BUT WE DIDN'T *MEAN* TO--

C'MON, FLOUNDER, IT'S....

I WOULDN'T *EXPECT* YOU TO UNDERSTAND. YOU'RE JUST A COUPLE OF *GIRLS.*

AWRIGHT! WAY TO GO, FLOUNDER!

WE WERE WORRIED ABOUT YOU A SECOND THERE, BUT YOU SURE SET THEM STRAIGHT!

YEAH. I SURE DID.

HI, SCUTTLE. WHAT'S *THAT*?

OH, *HI*, KID!

WELL, WHAT WE GOT HERE IS AN ANTIQUE CROUTONIOUS BERGLESNART. HUMANS USE IT TO SWAT *FLIES* WITH.

OOOOOOO!

I *TOLD* YOU HE KNOWS EVERYTHING, JENNY.

SCUTTLE, WE GOT A PROBLEM WE WANTED TO *ASK* YOU ABOUT...

KID, WHEN IT COMES TO PROBLEMS, MY NAME'S ALWAYS THE *FIRST* ONE THAT COMES TO MIND.

JENNY HERE IS INTERESTED... ROMANTICALLY... IN A PARTICULAR GUY. AND WE WERE HOPING *YOU* MIGHT GIVE US SOME TIPS ON WHAT GUYS LOOK FOR IN FEMALES.

OH, *I* GET IT. SOMETHING SURE-FIRE THAT JUST DRIVES GUYS WILD, *huh*?

SOMETHING LIKE THAT.

WELL YOU CAME TO THE *RIGHT* PLACE. I'M GONNA GIVE IT TO YOU IN *ONE* WORD.

YOU LISTENING?

WE'RE LISTENING.

WE'RE SURE.

'CAUSE I'M ONLY SAYING THIS *ONCE*, YOU SURE?

OKAY. ONE WORD.

FEATHERS.

FEATHERS?

ABSOLUTELY. IF YOU GOT CLEAN, GORGEOUS FEATHERS, *NO* MALE CAN RESIST YOU.

TRUST ME ON THIS. HUMAN WOMEN WEAR FEATHERS IN THEIR *HATS*. WE BIRDS GOT 'EM ALL OVER. WHY, FEATHERS DO *MORE* TO...

¿sniff-sniff¿ ...SOMEBODY LEAVE AN *OVEN* ON SOMEWHERE?

SCUTTLE! YOUR TAIL!!

YEEEOOOWWWTCH!!!

YOU OKAY, SCUTTLE?

OH, SURE, *SURE*, KID. I *MEANT* TO DO THAT. HONEST. *Uh...*

LOOK! FEATHERS!!

THAT'S IT! I MEANT TO CUT SOME FEATHERS LOOSE TO GIVE TO YOU GUYS. HERE YA GO.

NO PROBLEM, KID.

THANKS, SCUTTLE. YOU'RE THE *GREATEST*.

BUT YOU BETTER GET GOING! THAT'S A HUMAN FISHING SHIP. YOU DON'T WANT 'EM TO SEE YA.

OH. RIGHT.

THANKS AGAIN!

ANYTIME, PRINCESS.

BUT NOT ANYTIME REAL *SOON*, HUH?

OOOOOTCH!

ERIC, YOU SHOULDN'T STAND SO CLOSE. YOU NEVER KNOW IF...

WITH ANY LUCK, WE'LL GET A LOT CLOSER THAN *THIS*, GRIMS. WE'RE FINDING THAT *SHARK*.

BUT YOU DON'T KNOW FOR SURE THAT THIS "*MONSTER SHARK*" THAT WAS SIGHTED WAS THE ONE YOUR FATHER ENCOUNTERED SO LONG AGO.

I GOT A *FEELING* ABOUT IT, GRIMS. MY FATHER'S HARPOON CAME *THAT* CLOSER TO NAILING HIM.

LEFT A BIG SCAR, SO THE STORY GOES. WHICH MEANS HE'LL BE LOOKING TO *SETTLE* A SCORE. AND I'M TELLING YOU, GRIMSBY...

I'M GOING TO HAVE THE LAST LAUGH.

HA HA

HA

HA HA

"*FLOUNDER*, HOW DO YOU LIKE MY OUTFIT?" SHE SAYS!

MAYBE SHE THINKS SHE'S A FLYING FISH, HUH, GUYS?

SOGGY FEATHERS! I CAN'T *STAND* IT! BWAAAA HAHAHA!

I NEVER WANT TO SEE YOU OR YOUR STUPID BIRD FRIEND *AGAIN*!!

THAT REALLY WASN'T *NICE*, FLOUNDER. NEXT TIME YOU COME BY AND WANT TO SPEND TIME WITH ME, MAYBE I'LL JUST LAUGH AT *YOU* AND YOU'LL SEE HOW *YOU* LIKE IT.

HEY, FLOUNDER! YOU'RE NOT GONNA LET HER *UPSET* YOU, ARE YA?

UH... NO. OF COURSE NOT.

GREAT! SO... WHAT 'CHA WANNA *DO*?

ACTUALLY,... I THINK I'D JUST LIKE TO BE *ALONE* FOR A LITTLE. SEE YOU LATER, GUYS.

FLOUNDER! HAVE YOU SEEN *ARIEL*?

SURE, JUST A FEW MINUTES AGO. SHE WAS HEADING TOWARDS THE CASTLE.

NOW *DAT'S* A RELIEF! FOR ONCE, DA KING! ASKED ME TO DO SOMET'ING ...

AND I DIDN'T RUN INTO ANY *PROBLEMS* BECAUSE OF IT.

I'M SORRY I FOLLOWED YOU, FLOUNDER. IT WAS KIND OF SNEAKY, BUT I DIDN'T WANT TO JUST SWIM OFF MAD...

WELL YOU DON'T GET NO PROTEST FROM ME. IF YOU HADN'T STARTLED DAT SCARFACE, WE'D BE FISH-FOOD.

THE QUESTION IS, WHAT DO WE DO NOW? HOW DO WE GET OUT?

DERE'S A SMALL HOLE... BUT MY SHELL'S TOO HARD AND FLOUNDER'S TOO BIG TO FIT...

I CAN DO IT! I CAN GO GET HELP!

IF YOU'RE GONNA, THEN DO IT FAST. THAT SHARK'S POUNDING AT THE OTHER END... AND I THINK HE'S GONNA BREAK THROUGH!

HURRY UP!

FOR LONG MINUTES, SEBASTIAN AND FLOUNDER CRINGE AND WAIT... AND THEN...

THOOOM

HEY, SCARFACE! WHY SETTLE FOR A LIGHT SNACK WHEN YOU CAN HAVE A MAIN COURSE?

FASTER, ARIEL! FASTER!!

THAT HUMAN SHIP BETTER BE WHERE I REMEMBER IT... OR DADDY GETS ONE LESS DAUGHTER.

Merida

Disney · PIXAR
BRAVE

"MANY YEARS AGO, WHEN I WAS A WEE GIRL…"

"…ON A PERFECT DAY WITH MY PARENTS…"

"…MY FATHER FERGUS, THE KING, GAVE ME A BOW!"

"BUT AS I STARTED PRACTICING, I SAW SOMETHING IN THE FOREST!"

"SUDDENLY, *MOR'DU* THE BEAR SHOWED UP."

"...A DAY WHERE I CAN RIDE MY HORSE, ANGUS, THROUGH THE FOREST, PRACTICE MY ARCHERY, AND MAYBE EVEN CHANGE MY FATE."

THUNK

"IT ISN'T THAT BAD..."

"WELL IT WASN'T, UNTIL..."

...IT WAS THE BIGGEST BEAR I'VE EVER SEEN! HIS HIDE LITTERED WITH THE WEAPONS OF FALLEN WARRIORS...

...HIS FACE SCARRED WITH ONE DEAD EYE! I DREW MY SWORD AND...

...WOOSH! ONE SWIPE, HIS SWORD SHATTERED!

THEN CHOMP! DAD'S LEG WAS CLEAN OFF! DOWN THE MONSTER'S THROAT IT WENT!

MOR'DU HAS NEVER BEEN SEEN SINCE. HE'S ROAMING THE WILDS WAITING FOR HIS CHANCE TO GET REVENGE!

LET HIM RETURN. I'LL FINISH WHAT I GUDDLED IN THE FIRST PLACE!

ONCE, THERE WAS AN ANCIENT KINGDOM RULED BY A WISE KING...

OH, MUM...ANCIENT KINGDOM...

...HE DIVIDED THE KINGDOM AMONG HIS FOUR SONS.

BUT THE OLDEST WANTED TO RULE THE LAND FOR HIMSELF...

...AND THE KINGDOM FELL...

TA THUMP

THUMP

THUMP

THAT'S A NICE STORY.

IT'S NOT JUST A STORY. LEGENDS ARE LESSONS; THEY RING WITH TRUTH.

MAKE YOUR PEACE WITH THIS. THE CLANS **ARE** COMING TO PRESENT THEIR SUITORS...

IT'S NOT FAIR!

IT'S MARRIAGE, MERIDA. IT'S NOT THE END OF THE WORLD!

"AND SOON THE DAY ARRIVED..."

SO HERE WE ARE, EHM...THE FOUR CLANS...UH... GATHERING!

"MACINTOSH!"

I PRESENT MY HEIR AND SCION, WHO WITH HIS OWN SWORD VANQUISHED A THOUSAND FOES!

SWISH

"MACGUFFIN!

I PRESENT MY ELDEST SON, WHO WITH HIS BARE HANDS VANQUISHED **TWO**-THOUSAND FOES!

CRACK

"DINGWALL!"

I PRESENT MY ONLY SON, WHO TOOK OUT A WHOLE ARMADA SINGLE-HANDEDLY!

LIES!!

AH'AHA

WHAT? I HEARD THAT! SAY IT TO MY FACE!

SO LET THE GAMES BEGIN!

"THERE'S A REASON WHY I CHOSE **ARCHERY**"

"EVEN IF THEY CAN HIT THE TARGET..."

"...EVEN IF THEY CAN HIT A BULLSEYE..."

"...I CAN DO BETTER!"

I AM MERIDA, FIRST-BORN DESCENDANT OF CLAN DUNBROCH! AND I'LL BE SHOOTING FOR MY OWN HAND!

MERIDA! DON'T YOU **DARE**!

FFSSHHH

"I SHOULD HAVE KNOWN..."

"...IT WOULDN'T WORK."

YOU DON'T KNOW WHAT YOU'VE DONE! YOU EMBARRASSED THEM! YOU EMBARRASSED **ME!**

IT WILL BE FIRE AND SWORDS IF NOT SET RIGHT.

THIS IS UNFAIR! THIS WHOLE MARRIAGE IS WHAT YOU WANT. DO YOU EVER BOTHER TO ASK ME WHAT I WANT?

YOU ALWAYS TELL ME WHAT TO DO, TRYING TO MAKE ME LIKE YOU. WELL, I'M NOT GOING TO BE LIKE YOU!

YOU'RE ACTING LIKE A CHILD.

AND YOU'RE A...BEAST. THAT'S WHAT **YOU** ARE!

NO! STOP THAT!

I'LL NEVER BE LIKE YOU!

RIIIP

"I FOLLOWED THE WISPS..."

OH, SOMEBODY'S COME TO THE DOOR!

OH!

SWISS

WELCOME TO THE CRAFTY CARVER, FOR ALL YOUR BEAR-THEMED CARVINGS AND ITEMS.

WHO ARE YOU?

JUST A HUMBLE WOOD CARVER.

BUT THE WILL O' THE WISPS... THEY LEAD YOU TO YOUR FATE!

NO, THEY LEAD YOU TO BARGAINS. AND I'M WILLING TO BARTER.

YOUR BROOM... IT'S SWEEPING BY ITSELF!

THAT'S SILLY. I'M A WIT--I MEAN, A WHITTLER.

SPELLS ARE HER SPECIALTY.

THE CROW TALKS! YOU'RE A WITCH!

YOU'LL GIVE ME A SPELL... IT'S MY MOTHER--

NO, I'M A WOOD CARVER.

GET OUT! SHOO!

WAIT! I'LL BUY IT ALL, EVERY CARVING!

HOW WILL YOU PAY FOR IT?

WITH THIS. I'LL BUY EVERY CARVING...AND ONE SPELL.

I WANT A SPELL TO CHANGE MY MUM, THAT WILL CHANGE MY FATE.

I GOT THIS RING FROM A PRINCE. HE WANTED A SPELL, STRENGTH OF TEN MEN. CHANGED HIS FATE.

"SO, AFTER THE WITCH ACCEPTED THE PAYMENT..."

NOW I NEED JUST A LITTLE BIT OF THIS...

AND THIS...

AND THIS...

HMM... YES!

BOOM

A CAKE? IF MY MUM EATS THIS, SHE WILL CHANGE?

OH, AND WHAT WAS THAT THING ABOUT THE SPELL....STRENGTH OF TEN MEN? OH, WELL...

WAIT! WHAT?! SHE DISAPPEARED...

"I HEADED BACK TO THE CASTLE. I HAD TO GIVE IT A TRY..."

WHERE HAVE YOU BEEN? I WAS SO WORRIED.

I MADE THIS FOR YOU. IT'S A PEACE OFFERING...

YOU MADE THIS FOR ME?

MMM... INTERESTING FLAVOR.

HOW DO YOU FEEL? HAVE YOU CHANGED YOUR MIND ABOUT THE MARRIAGE?

WHY DON'T WE GO UPSTAIRS TO THE LORDS AND PUT THIS WHOLE KERFUFFLE TO REST?

"NOTHING HAPPENED..."

OHH...SUDDENLY, I'M NOT SO WELL.

H-HOW DO YOU FEEL ABOUT THE MARRIAGE NOW?

JUST TAKE ME TO MY ROOM WHILE YOUR FATHER IS ENTERTAINING THE LORDS...

?

A LITTLE TO THE LEFT! THAT'S GOOD! LOOK OUT, YOU MANKY BEAR!

MOR'DU! MOR'DU! MOR'DU!

MY LADY QUEEN, WE'VE BEEN WAITING PATIENTLY, BUT NOW...

BURP

M'LORDS, I'M... OUT OF SORTS AT THE MOMENT. IF YOU'LL EXCUSE ME...

ELINOR, LOOK! IT'S MOR'DU!

ARE YOU ALL RIGHT, ELINOR?

I'M FINE...GO BACK TO AVENGING YOUR LEG.

AYE, YOU HEARD HER, LADS!

JUST TAKE ALL THE TIME YOU NEED GETTING YOURSELF RIGHT, MUM.

MMM

MUM?

FRUSH

BAM

YEAAHHHH!

WILL YOU LISTEN TO ME? WE CAN'T GO THIS WAY!

QUICK!

"WE NEED TO GET OUT OF THE CASTLE NOW!"

"BUT WHO CAN I TURN TO?"

A WITCH TURNED MUM INTO A BEAR! IT'S NOT MY FAULT! WE'VE GOT TO GET OUT! I NEED YOUR HELP!

"I ADMIT IT... THEY ARE GOOD!"

"FIRST THEY TRAP DAD AND THE LORDS ON TOP OF THE ROOF..."

IT'S LOCKED!

"I CANT BELIEVE IT, I FOUND IT!"

NO! SHE WAS JUST HERE!

NO NO NO!

THUNK

PLINK

WELCOME TO THE CRAFTY CARVER. I AM COMPLETELY OUT OF STOCK. IF YOU NEED A PREORDER, POUR VIAL ONE INTO THE CAULDRON...

...VIAL TWO IF YOU SPEAK GAELLIC, AND VIAL THREE IF YOU'RE THAT REDHEADED LASS.

PRINCESS, I WON'T BE BACK 'TIL SPRING. THERE IS ONE BIT I FORGOT TO TELL YOU ABOUT THE SPELL...

PLOOP PLOOP PLOOP

BY THE SECOND SUNRISE YOUR SPELL WILL BE PERMANENT UNLESS YOU REMEMBER THESE WORDS...

FATE BE CHANGED, LOOK INSIDE. MEND THE BOND, TORN BY PRIDE.

"...A STORMY NIGHT LONG AGO"

"A HUGE CRACK OF THUNDER FRIGHTENED ME. I RAN TO MUM."

A BRAVE WEE LASSIE, I AM HERE.

KRACK

"I'LL NEVER FORGET HER WORDS."

I'LL ALWAYS BE RIGHT HERE.

"THE MORNING AFTER IS...STRANGE..."

SPUT SPUT

THOSE BERRIES ARE POISONOUS, MUM!

"...IT'S MY TURN TO GIVE THE LESSONS."

HOW DO YOU KNOW YOU DON'T LIKE IT UNLESS YOU TRY IT?

"AND FUNNY..."

"WE FINALLY FIND SOMETHING TO BOND OVER."

"WE ARE HAVING A GREAT TIME!"

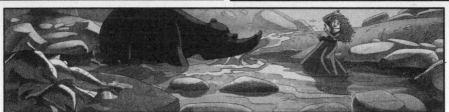

"BUT THEN SOMETHING HAPPENS."

HEY, WHERE ARE YOU GOING?

GRRR

AHH! MUM...?

SNIFF SNIFF

LIKE THE TAPESTRY! THE SPELL HAS HAPPENED BEFORE!

THE OLDEST, THE WILLFUL PRINCE... SPLIT LIKE...

STRENGTH OF TEN MEN... THE INSIDE WILL BECOME THE OUTSIDE...

OH NO! THE PRINCE BECAME...

GRrrr

...MOR'DU!

ROARrr

"WE JUST NEED A WAY INTO THE CASTLE..."

ALL CLEAR...

WHAT'S GOING ON?

NO MORE TALK! NO MORE TRADITIONS! WE SETTLE THIS NOW!

NONE OF YOUR SONS ARE FIT TO MARRY MY DAUGHTER!

YAAAAH

THEN OUR ALLIANCE IS OVER! THIS MEANS WAR!

THEY'RE GOING TO MURDER EACH OTHER!

OUR CLANS WERE ONCE ENEMIES, BUT WHEN WE WERE THREATENED FROM THE SEA, YOU JOINED **TOGETHER** TO DEFEND OUR LANDS.

IT WAS AN ALLIANCE FORGED IN BRAVERY AND FRIENDSHIP.

BUT I'VE BEEN SELFISH. I TORE A GREAT RIFT IN OUR BOND. AND I KNOW I HAVE TO MEND MY MISTAKE.

SO I ACCEPT THE TRADITION AND PLEDGE TO MARRY INTO ONE OF YOUR CLA...

"I'M ABOUT TO SAY IT..."

"...WHEN MUM STARTS MIMING SOMETHING TO ME!"

OR PERHAPS THERE'S ANOTHER WAY? THAT WE MIGHT DARE TO... BREAK TRADITION?

THE QUEEN FEELS WE SHOULD BE FREE TO...WRITE OUR OWN STORY.

FOLLOW OUR OWN HEARTS. AND FIND LOVE IN OUR OWN TIME.

THAT'S -:SNIFF:- BEAUTIFUL!

THIS IS--

THE QUEEN AND I PUT THE DECISION TO YOU, MY LORDS. MIGHT OUR YOUNG PEOPLE DECIDE FOR THEMSELVES WHOM THEY WILL LOVE?

THIS IS A GRAND IDEA!

AYE, WHY SHOULDN'T WE CHOOSE?

THIS SETTLES IT! LET THESE LADS TRY AND WIN HER HEART BEFORE THEY WIN HER HAND... IF THEY CAN!

EVERYONE TO THE CELLAR! LET'S CRACK OPEN THE KING'S PRIVATE RESERVES TO CELEBRATE!

YEAHHH!

BRING THE TINY GLASSES...

AND NOW...

HYAH!

"I HAVE TO HELP MUM."

MAUDIE, I NEED YOU!

UH? OH NO...

"I REALLY MESSED UP THIS TIME, BUT MAYBE..."

"...THEY CAN HELP ME AGAIN!"

AHHH!

WAIT...WHERE IS THE THIRD ONE?

?!

"THEY MADE IT!"

I'M COMING, MUM!

"I JUST HOPE IT'S NOT TOO LATE..."

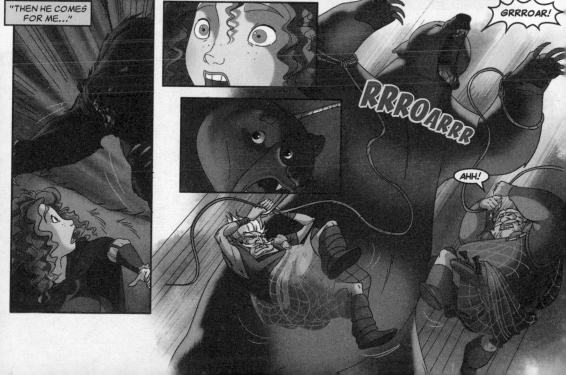

I DON'T UNDERSTAND. I RESTORED WHAT WAS TORN. WHY HAVEN'T YOU CHANGED?

...

I MENDED THE BOND... DIDN'T I?

OH MUM, I'M SORRY... THIS IS ALL MY FAULT! I DID THIS TO YOU... TO US...

YOU'VE ALWAYS BEEN THERE FOR ME. YOU'VE NEVER GIVEN UP! I JUST WANT YOU BACK, MUM!

I LOVE YOU.

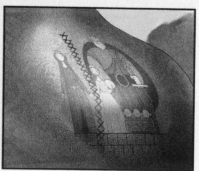

MUM! MUM YOU'RE BACK! YOU'VE CHANGED!

NO, SWEETHEART... WE DID.

ELINOR?!

BOYS?!!

HAHAH

"THE WITCH WAS RIGHT, THERE ARE NO WEE WISHES."

WELCOME, BELOVED FRIEND *POWHATAN.*

PEACE, KEKATA. IT'S GOOD TO BE HOME.

THE MASSAWOMECKS ARE DEFEATED! WITH THE HELP OF OUR BROTHERS, OUR VILLAGE IS SAFE AGAIN!

WHERE IS MY DAUGHTER?

YOU KNOW POCAHONTAS...

"...SHE HAS HER MOTHER'S SPIRIT. SHE GOES WHEREVER THE WIND TAKES HER."

POCAHONTAS!

YOUR FATHER'S BACK! COME DOWN HERE!

HE'S BACK, *FLIT!* COME ON, MEEKO!

SHOW OFF!

WHAT WERE YOU DOING UP THERE?

THINKING.

ABOUT THAT *DREAM* AGAIN? HAVE YOU FIGURED IT OUT YET?

I KNOW IT MEANS *SOMETHING*. I JUST DON'T KNOW *WHAT*.

YOU SHOULD ASK YOUR FATHER ABOUT IT.

HMM... MAYBE I SHOULD.

WE'D BETTER GO BACK.

EVEN THE WILD MOUNTAIN STREAM MUST SOMEDAY JOIN THE BIG RIVER.

YOUR MOTHER WORE THIS FOR OUR WEDDING. IT WAS HER DREAM TO SEE YOU WEAR IT AT YOUR OWN.

IT SUITS YOU.

HE WANTS ME TO BE STEADY, LIKE THE RIVER.

BUT THE RIVER'S NOT STEADY AT ALL.

I NEED TO SEE WHAT'S AROUND THE RIVER BEND.

SHOULD I CHOOSE THE SMOOTH AND STEADY COURSE? SHOULD I MARRY KOCOUM?

OR DOES MY DREAMGIVER STILL WAIT FOR ME JUST AROUND THE RIVER BEND?

GREAT POWHATAN, I WILL LEAD OUR WARRIORS TO THE RIVER AND *ATTACK!*

WE WILL DESTROY THESE WARRIORS THE WAY WE DESTROYED THE MASSAWOMECKS.

KOCOUM, IN THAT BATTLE, WE KNEW OUR ENEMY. BUT THESE PALE VISITORS ARE STRANGE TO US.

TAKE SOME MEN AND OBSERVE THEM. LET US HOPE THEY DO NOT INTEND TO STAY.

...JAMESTOWN!

I HEREBY CLAIM THIS LAND AND *ALL* OF ITS RICHES IN THE NAME OF *KING JAMES* THE FIRST AND DO SO NAME THIS SETTLEMENT...

WELL, IT APPEARS I'VE SELECTED A PERFECT LOCATION. NOT A SAVAGE IN SIGHT.

JUST BECAUSE WE DON'T SEE THEM DOESN'T MEAN THEY'RE NOT OUT THERE.

WELL PERHAPS YOU SHOULD VENTURE FORTH AND DETERMINE THEIR WHEREABOUTS, HMM?

YES, SIR.

NOW, GENTLEMEN, TO WORK!

LET'S GET STARTED.

YOU MEN GET THE SHIP UNLOADED!

YOU MEN BUILD THE FORT!

YOU START CLEARING THE SHRUBBERY!

THE REST OF YOU GET THE SHOVELS AND START DIGGING!

DIGGING FOR WHAT?

FOR *GOLD!* MOUNTAINS OF IT!

FOR *YEARS* THE SPANISH HAVE BEEN RAVAGING THE NEW WORLD OF ITS MOST PRECIOUS RESOURCES.

BUT NOW IT'S *OUR* TURN!

GRAB A PICK AND SHOVEL, MEN, AND DIG TILL YOU DROP!

IT'S ALL THERE FOR THE TAKING! ALL YOU HAVE TO DO IS FIND THE MOTHERLODE!

ALL OF MY LIFE I'VE BEEN SEARCHING FOR A LAND LIKE THIS!

A WILD, UNTAMED LAND.

A LAND WHERE A MAN WHO THIRSTS FOR ADVENTURE CAN...

!

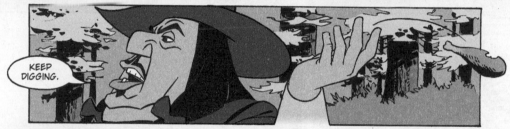

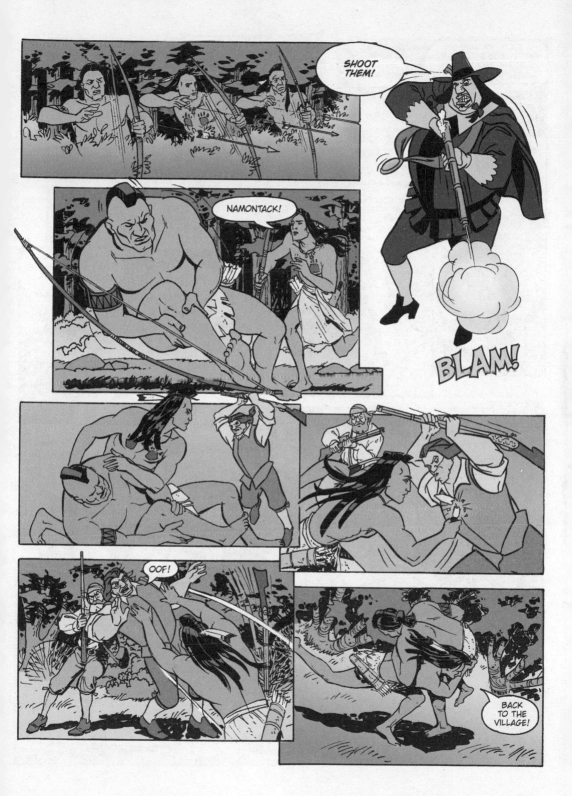

FOLLOW HIM. I WANT TO KNOW WHERE HE'S SNEAKING OFF TO.

YES, SIR.

AND IF YOU SEE ANY INDIANS, *SHOOT* THEM!

YOU'VE BEEN A POOR EXCUSE FOR A SOLDIER, DON'T DISAPPOINT ME AGAIN.

AT KOCOUM'S HUT.

KOCOUM! I THINK POCAHONTAS IS IN *TROUBLE!*

YOU HAVE TO COME WITH ME AND TALK TO MY FATHER.

TALKING ISN'T GOING TO DO ANY GOOD.

MY MEN ARE PLANNING TO ATTACK YOUR PEOPLE.

MAYBE IT'S NOT TOO LATE TO STOP THIS.

~AHEM!~ *NOW* THEN, THERE'S SOMETHING I WANT TO SHOW YOU. *LOOK!*

THE RIPPLES...

SO SMALL AT FIRST...

...THEN LOOK HOW THEY GROW.

BUT SOMEONE HAS TO START THEM.

THEY'RE NOT GOING TO LISTEN TO US.

ONLY WHEN THE FIGHTING STOPS CAN YOU BE TOGETHER.

LET'S GO TALK TO YOUR FATHER.

POCAHONTAS WANTS TO LOOK INTO THE EYES OF THE MAN WHO KILLED KOCOUM.

BE QUICK.

POCAHONTAS!

I'M SO SORRY.

IF WE'D NEVER MET, NONE OF THIS WOULD HAVE HAPPENED.

DON'T CRY. I'D RATHER DIE TOMORROW THAN LIVE 100 YEARS WITHOUT KNOWING YOU.

NO MATTER WHAT HAPPENS TO ME, I'LL ALWAYS BE WITH YOU...

...FOREVER.

I'VE GOT TO SEE GRANDMOTHER WILLOW.

THE END

WHAT'S HE SO *CRABBY* ABOUT, MAMA? WE'RE THE ONES WHO GOT TURNED INTO *FURNITURE* AND *DISHES!*

I RATHER THINK *WE* GOT THE *BEST* OF THE LOT, MY DEAR. I DON'T THINK *I* EVER LOOKED *BETTER!*

WELL NO ONE ASKED *ME!* I WISH I'D BEEN TURNED INTO A *BIG FEROCIOUS BEAST!*

NOTHING HAS CHANGED...

OUR LIVES ARE JUST THE SAME AS THEY ALWAYS WERE.

Mais oui! WE ARE TRULY *DEDICATED!*

I CERTAINLY HAVE *NOTHING* BETTER TO DO WITH MY TIME!

I *STILL* SAY HE'S A *CRAB!*

I CAN'T SAY THE MASTER IS VERY MUCH CHANGED, EITHER.

OUI! THE TANTRUMS HE THREW AS A *CHILD* WERE *NO* LESS FIERCE!

MUST YOU TALK SO *LOUD,* LUMIERE?

I *SPEAK MY MIND,* UNLIKE *YOU,* I DO NOT *HESITATE!*

I'LL HAVE YOU KNOW I HAVEN'T LOST A *SECOND* IN ALL THIS TIME!

THE POOR SOUL WAS *ALWAYS* ON THE WRONG FOOT.

THE MASTER MUST HAVE PULLED A *LULU* TO GET US INTO THIS FIX!

IT'S *TRUE* HE WAS NOT THE *FRIENDLIEST* CHILD!

WOULDN'T GIVE A BEGGAR THE *TIME OF DAY!*

TELL ME *MORE* ABOUT THE *YOUNG PRINCE,* MAMA!

WELL... I'M NOT SPEAKING OF TIME AS COGSWORTH MARKS IT, BUT IT WAS *LONG, LONG AGO...*

WE HAVEN'T SEEN THE END OF IT YET. MARK MY WORDS, THERE'S STILL MORE CHANGES TO COME.

KNOCK ON WOOD.

YOU'RE GETTING WAX ON ME!

WELL, I STILL DON'T SEE WHAT HE'S ALWAYS SO CRABBY ABOUT!

SHHHHH!

DO YOU WANT HIM TO HEAR YOU?

MRS. POTTS?

YES, MASTER?

I CAN'T FIND MUSIC BOX. HAVE YOU SEEN HIM?

I DO BELIEVE I HEARD HIM SINGING IN THE LIBRARY. YOU GO HAVE A LOOK, MASTER.

THERE'S YOUR ANSWER, CHIP. INSIDE THERE'S STILL A LITTLE BOY WHO HASN'T HAD HIS NAP.

"BOTHERED"

FATHER! WHAT ARE YOU DOING WITH *PIERRE*?!!

HE IS AN *ESSENTIAL PART OF MY* INVENTION!

Disney's *Beauty AND THE BEAST*

HE IS THE *LOCATOR MECHANISM* FOR THE WORLD'S FIRST FULLY AUTOMATIC *TRUFFLE HARVESTER!*

PIERRE'S SENSITIVE NOSE DETECTS THE *TANTALIZING AROMA* OF HIS *FAVORITE DELICACY...*

HIS WRIGGLES OF EXCITEMENT TRIP *THIS LEVER* WHICH DROPS THE BAG OF SAND ONTO THIS *SPIKE*, WHICH SPLITS THE BAG AND SPILLS THE SAND INTO THIS *HOPPER*. IT POURS INTO THESE CUPS WHICH THEN TURNS THIS WHEEL CONNECTED TO THE MECHANISM WHICH DRIVES THESE POWERFUL DIGGING BLADES...

THE DIRT *PASSES THROUGH HERE* WHERE IT IS SIFTED THROUGH THIS MESH AND THE *TRUFFLES* ARE PLUCKED OUT AND DEPOSITED IN THIS *BUCKET.*

THEY MIGHT GET A BIT *MANGLED*, BUT THEN THEY GET CHOPPED UP ANYWAY.

ISN'T THAT A LOT OF TROUBLE FOR A *TRIFLING TRUFFLE*?

RICH PEOPLE PAY A *KING'S RANSOM* FOR THESE LITTLE TIDBITS, MY DEAR.

I KNOW ALL MY IDEAS HAVEN'T BEEN *PRAC-TICAL*, BELLE, BUT THIS TIME...

...OUR FORTUNE IS *ASSURED!*

NOW PUT THAT BOOK AWAY. THE DAY IS MUCH TOO FINE FOR YOU TO BE *IN HERE!*

I'M HAPPY WHERE I AM, PAPA!

YOU SHOULD BE *OUTSIDE* PLAYING WITH THE *OTHER CHILDREN!*

I'M HAVING A MUCH BETTER TIME IN *KING ARTHUR'S COURT!*

SOMETIMES I CAN SEE MYSELF LIVING IN A CASTLE *SURROUNDED BY SERVANTS.*

I MIGHT EVEN ENTERTAIN THE THOUGHT OF A *HANDSOME PRINCE...*

...AS LONG AS HE WAS *GENTLE,* AND *KIND...* NOT LIKE THOSE CHILDISH ROUGHNECKS IN THE *SQUARE!* NOT ONE OF THEM COULD EVEN *SPELL GALLANT!*

A DAY WILL COME WHEN THOSE BOYS WILL LOOK LIKE *KNIGHTS IN SHINING ARMOR* TO YOU.

NEVER! I WON'T HAVE ANYTHING TO DO WITH THEM! MEN ARE SUCH... SUCH...

HEAR THAT, PIERRE? ACCORDING TO MY DAUGHTER THERE ISN'T AN *OUNCE OF DIFFERENCE BETWEEN US!*

OINK!

WELL, I SUPPOSE THERE ARE *SOME* EXCEPTIONS.

GRRRR!

OH!

I GUESS I'M NOT *ALONE* ENOUGH!

WELL, I'M THE ONE WHO *WANTED* HER LIFE TO BE MORE LIKE A *FAIRY TALE*...

HERE I AM *STUCK*, JUST LIKE *RAPUNZEL* IMPRISONED IN HER TOWER!

THERE MUST BE *SOMETHING* MORE TO LIFE THAN THIS!

I DON'T SUPPOSE I CAN COUNT ON BEING *RESCUED*. THERE ARE NO *MAGICAL GUARDIANS* AROUND THESE PARTS.

RUMBLE... RUMBLE!!

AND NO *GALLANT KNIGHTS* ON POWERFUL CHARGERS ROAMING THE COUNTRYSIDE LOOKING FOR DAMSELS IN DISTRESS.

CRAASH!!

PIERRE!!!??

OINK!

BELLE! YOU'RE NOT A *TRUFFLE*!

BUT JUST FOR A MOMENT, PRETEND YOU *WERE A TRUFFLE*, MY DEAR! YOU CAN SEE JUST HOW *MAGNIFICENT A SUCCESS* MY INVENTION WILL BE!

I HAVE NO NEED TO *PRETEND*, PAPA. MY LIFE IS AS FANTASTIC AS *ANYTHING* IN STORYBOOKS.

OINK!

Disney's Beauty AND THE BEAST

BEWILDERED

HE'S *NOCTURNAL* NOW, YOU KNOW, AND *MUSIC BOX* IS THE ONLY THING THAT BRINGS THE POOR SOUL ANY *COMFORT.*

HE'S BEEN SITTING THERE FOR *HOURS!* DOESN'T HE KNOW HOW *LATE* IT'S GETTING?

WHO *WAS* MUSIC BOX, MAMA? I DON'T REMEMBER HIM.

MUSIC BOX WAS *NEVER* HUMAN, DEAR. HE'S ALWAYS BEEN THE MASTER'S *FAVORITE TOY!*

HE SURE SINGS *PRETTY!*

HMMF! PRIMITIVE CREATURE! HAS TO BE RE-WOUND CONSTANTLY!

THE LITTLE DARLING HAS *CHARMS* THAT DO WHAT *NONE* OF THE REST OF US CAN!

YAWN! I'M READY FOR THE CUPBOARD, MAMA. COME *TUCK ME UP*

SUCH A *SAD SONG,* MASTER! MUST WE HAVE IT *AGAIN* AND AGAIN?

IT *SOOTHES* ME.

AHHH, BUT *MUSIC* WAS MADE FOR *LOVE!* A SONG IN YOUR HEART COULD BE JUST THE *THING* TO *BREAK THE SPELL!*

MASTER, DO NOT STOP NOW!

YOU WERE DOING SO WELL!

SHE WAS LAUGHING AT ME!

NON, NON, MASTER! YOUR FUR, IT WAS TICKLING ME!

YOU MUST BE PATIENT, HIGHNESS! THIS LOVE-- IT TAKES TIME!

EXACTLY WHAT I WAS ABOUT TO SAY?

IT'S HOPELESS! WHO COULD LOVE THIS??!

YOU HAVE PLEASING ATTRIBUTES! YOU'RE BIG AND STRONG!

STRONG ENOUGH TO TEAR A MAN LIMB FROM LIMB!

PERHAPS A DIFFERENT APPROACH, YOUR HIGHNESS. TALK TO HER SWEETLY!

I--DON'T KNOW WHAT TO SAY.

WE ARE SURROUNDED WITH WORDS. YOU HAVE ONLY TO CHOOSE A BEAUTIFUL POEM AND MELT THE FAIR COQUETTE INTO A WARM, SOFT LUMP!

OOOOHHH!

UGHH!

THERE WAS A TIME WHEN THESE BOOKS MEANT MORE TO ME THAN ANYTHING IN THE WORLD!...

I DON'T KNOW WHAT'S IN THEM ANYMORE.

HAVE *YOU* ANY NOTIONS, COGSWORTH?

WELL.... *ahem*... IF I MIGHT MAKE A RECOMMENDATION...

I MYSELF HAVE *ahem!* HAD THE OCCASION TO UTILIZE THE WORDS OF THE POETS...

THERE IS *NOTHING* KNOWN TO INTEREST A MAIDEN MORE THAN A *FLATTERING COMPARISON!*

I AM FOND OF SUCH A THING *MYSELF!*

YOU WANT *ME* TO...??!

SPEAK IT AS THOUGH IT IS QUINTESSENTIALLY YOUR EXPRESS INTENTION!

SAY WHAT YOU *MEAN*, COGSWORTH!

I THOUGHT I MADE MYSELF CLEAR!

WE ARE SPEAKING OF AMOUR, NOT TIMETABLES!

SILENCE!!

HOW CAN I SPEAK OF *LOVE* WITH YOUR INCESSANT BABBLE ABOUT *ROMANCE??!!*

AAAAAARROOO

AND NOW THERE WILL BE NO MORE MUSIC.

PERHAPS WE CAN PUT HIM BACK TOGETHER.

HE WASN'T LIKE THE REST OF US, BUT HE HAD A HEART ALL THE SAME.

LUMIERE... DO YOU THINK THE PRINCE STILL HAS ONE?

AAAARRROOOO

I HOPE SO, MY FRIEND, BUT WE MAY NEED SOME HELP TO FIND IT.

WALT DISNEY'S
Cinderella's CHRISTMAS PARTY

PRESENTING A CLASSIC TALE THAT TOOK PLACE LONG, LONG **BEFORE** CINDERELLA EVER MET PRINCE CHARMING!

PREPARATIONS FOR CHRISTMAS VACATION ARE UNDERWAY, AND SEVERAL MICE WE KNOW ARE CURIOUS...

CINDERELLA! CINDERELLA! CINDERELLA!

YC 6401

PRESS THIS!

CLEAN THESE!

SEW THESE!

POLISH THIS!

WHEN YOU FINISH WITH THE GIRLS, I HAVE A **FEW** THINGS FOR YOU TO DO.

IT'S LATE, AND ONLY ONE LIGHT REMAINS IN THE OLD CHATEAU WHERE CINDERELLA LIVES WITH HER STEPMOTHER AND STEPSISTERS.

OH, DEAR! WILL I **EVER** FINISH?

BUT IT'S WORTH ALL THIS WORK TO GET A VACATION IN THE SUNNY SOUTH!

WHAT'S ALL THE FUSS FUSS?

HUMANS GOING TO SUNNY SOUTH FOR CHRISTMAS VACATION!

CINDERELLA GO TOO, GET REST FROM WORK!

SIT IN SUN ALL DAY AND EAT CHEESE!

WE MISS CINDERELLA, BUT GLAD SHE HAVE NICE WARM CHRISTMAS!

ZUK ZUK!

THE CHRISTMAS-VACATION PREPARATIONS GO ON AND ON...

CLUMSY! MIND THE WRINKLES!

LATE AT NIGHT, CINDERELLA DOES HER OWN PACKING...

OH, I AM *SO* WEARY ...BUT TOMORROW WE'RE OFF FOR THE SUNNY SOUTH!

HURRY, GIRLS! OUR SLEIGH IS HERE!

DON'T FORGET THE CAT!

DON'T FORGET *ME!*

WE ARE READY, PIERRE.

BUT...?

SORRY, CHILD; THERE ISN'T ROOM FOR YOU!

!

OH, *NO!*

POOR CINDERELLA!

STUNNED, CINDERELLA WATCHES THE SLEIGH GLIDE AWAY WITH HER STEPMOTHER AND STEPSISTERS...

OHHHH!

WHAT WILL I DO...?

THE FORLORN GIRL BROODS FOR QUITE A WHILE. AND THEN HER CHIN LIFTS...

I *KNOW* WHAT I'LL DO!

THE CHATEAU MICE HOLD AN EMERGENCY MEETING...

POOR CINDERELLA!

MEAN STEPMOTHER ABANDON HER!

CHRISTMAS COMING AND CINDERELLA ALL ALONE!

SNIFF!

GIRL MICE TAKE CHARGE OF SURPRISE PRESENT FOR CINDERELLA!

THE GIRL MICE BEGIN THEIR CHRISTMAS CAMPAIGN IN THE LIBRARY OF THE OLD CHATEAU...

PUSH... HARDER!

OOOF!

OH! *THAT* ONE!

Milady's Modiste

THAT'S WHAT WE MAKE FOR CINDERELLA'S PRESENT!

WON'T SHE BE *SURPRISED!*

FROM THE WHISPERINGS AND SQUEAKINGS IN THE WALLS AND WOODWORK, CINDERELLA KNOWS HER MICE FRIENDS ARE UP TO SOMETHING...

I JUST KNOW THE LITTLE DEARS ARE PREPARING SOME SORT OF SURPRISE FOR ME...

...BUT THEY DON'T KNOW I'M FIXING A SURPRISE FOR *THEM!*

NONE THE WISER, THE MICE GO ON WITH THEIR WORK...

START WITH KITCHEN BECAUSE THIS WHERE CINDERELLA SPEND MOST TIME!

BESIDES, NICE AND WARM HERE!

BESIDES BESIDES, NEARER TO EATS HERE!

JAQ LEADS THE CHRISTMAS TREE PATROL...

HUP... TOOP... THREEP... FOURP...

PATROL, HALT!

THIS ONE!

ZUK ZUK!

WITH THE HELP OF A BEAVER AND A FAWN, THE CHRISTMAS TREE IS CUT AND HAULED TO THE CHATEAU...

OH, WHAT A BEAUTY!

IN A LITTLE WHILE...

THERE! IT'S READY FOR THE TRIMMINGS!

WE TRIM!

AND THEY TRIM WITH VIM!

MEANWHILE, THE GIRL MICE ARE NOT IDLE...

OOH! PRETTY!

SOON WE HAVE ENOUGH TO START CINDERELLA'S CHRISTMAS SURPRISE!

ALMOST ENOUGH...

LOOK! FIND THINGS IN OLD MAGPIE NEST!

WON'T CINDERELLA BE SURPRISED WITH *THIS?*

MEANWHILE, CINDERELLA PREPARES HER OWN CHRISTMAS SURPRISE PARTY FOR HER LITTLE MICE FRIENDS...

NEW DRESSES FOR THE GIRLS... NEW JACKETS FOR THE BOYS...

AND GOODIES FOR ALL— CHEESE PUFFS, CHEESE TWISTS, CHEESE PETITS FOURS, CHEESE ECLAIRS, CHEESE DROPS, CHEESE CHEWS... AND LOTS OF JUST PLAIN CHEESE!

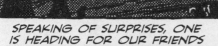

SPEAKING OF SURPRISES, ONE IS HEADING FOR OUR FRIENDS RIGHT NOW!

PREPARATIONS FOR THE DOUBLE CHRISTMAS PARTY CONTINUE, UNSUSPECTING...

WON'T THE LITTLE DEARS BE SURPRISED!

WON'T CINDERELLA BE SURPRISED!

MEANWHILE, OUTSIDE THE CHATEAU, ANOTHER SURPRISE IS IN THE MAKING...

THE MINSTREL MICE TUNE UP...

FOL-LOW ME IN MERRY MEAS-URE, FA LA LA LA LA LA LA LA

WHILE I TELL OF YULE-TIDE TREAS-URE, FA LA LA LA LA LA LA LA LA

687

MUSIC WITHIN...
MYSTERY WITHOUT...

ALMOST READY...

I HOPE I'M NOT FORGETTING ANY...

SOMEONE AT THE DOOR...?

I'M ALMOST AFRAID TO OPEN...

BUT IT MIGHT BE SOMEONE IN TROUBLE...

OH, WHAT*EVER* WILL I *DO?*

ZUK ZUK!

DON'T WORRY! WE FIX!

GETTING THROUGH TO A MAGIC-FREE FAIRY PROVES DIFFICULT...

...NO PRESENTS FOR MY GODCHILDREN... ⇒SOB⇒

DON'T FRET! WE FIND!

AT ONCE A TASK FORCE SETS OUT TO COMB THE COUNTRYSIDE...

WE FIND...

AND ANOTHER FORCE BEGINS AN INCH-BY-INCH SEARCH OF THE CHATEAU...

WE FIND!

Snuff

LACKADAY! AT THE END OF THE DAY, THE MAGIC WAND IS STILL MISSING!

⇒SIGH⇒

⇒SOB⇒

INDEED. AND IF THE PRINCE *HONORS* THAT TRADITION AND *DROWNS*, WHILE WE ALL SIT HERE *SAFELY*...

THE CHANCES ARE THE GRAND ADMIRAL WILL MAKE SURE *YOUR* NEXT ASSIGNMENT IS TO A *GARBAGE SCOW*.

YOUR HIGHNESS! GET *OFF* THAT THING! NO SENSE IN LOSING THE *BOTH* OF YE!

MUUUUUUUCH BETTER.

ERIC, YOU CERTAINLY TOOK YOUR TIME.

HAD TO MAKE SURE EVERYONE WAS *SAFE*, GRIMS. BUT NO ONE'S GOING TO BE ANY SAFER IN THE FUTURE IF WORKMANSHIP LIKE *THAT* KEEPS UP. *LOOK* AT THAT.

THAT HOLE DIDN'T COME FROM *HITTING* ANYTHING. WE WOULD HAVE FELT THE IMPACT. THE WOOD JUST *BUCKLED*. THAT'S POOR WORKMANSHIP.

GRIMS, THE FIRST THING I WANT DONE WHEN WE GET TO LAND IS HAVE OUR CURRENT *SHIPBUILDER FIRED*. AFTER THAT, I WANT TO SEE THE *GRAND ADMIRAL*.

I WANT A *NEW* SHIPBUILDER HIRED IMMEDIATELY. PUT OUT WORD THAT WE'LL INTERVIEW *ALL* INTERESTED PARTIES.

AT *ONCE*, ERIC.

I *WON'T* HAVE MY SAILORS ENDANGERED.

"shhhh..."

"OKAY. COAST IS CLEAR. LET'S GO."

"I DON'T SUPPOSE THERE'S, LIKE, SOME WAY I COULD TALK YOU *OUT* OF THIS, HUH?"

"NOT THAT I'M *AFRAID*, Y'UNDERSTAND. I'M NOT THE *LEAST* BIT AFRAID. I'M JUST CURIOUS. NEVER *AFRAID*. UH... CAN I TALK YOU *OUT* OF THIS?"

"NOPE."

"I WAS *AFRAID* OF THAT."

"AND JUST WHERE DO YOU T'INK YOU'RE GOING?"

"SEBASTIAN! WHEW... WHAT A RELIE..."

"I MEAN... OH, *DARN!* CAUGHT IN THE ACT!"

I PRESENT TO YOU THE WORLD'S *FIRST SUBMERSIBLE BOAT.* NO LONGER WILL THE LOWER DEPTHS BE THE ENEMY OF SAILORS WHO ARE LIMITED TO THE *SURFACE* OF THE SEAS.

THE SUBMERSIBLE CAN GO ANYWHERE A *FISH* CAN GO. IT CARRIES A FISHING NET IN ITS BELLY, A WIRE-POON FOR *LARGE* GAME...

BWWAAAA-HA-HA-HA HAA!!!

YOU'RE...YOU'RE ACTUALLY *SERIOUS?!* AN *UNDERWATER* SHIP?

I DON'T UNDERSTAND WHAT'S SO *FUNNY.*

THE THING A SAILOR DREADS MORE THAN ANYTHING ELSE IS *SINKING*... AND YOU WANT ME TO TRY AND GET MY MEN INTO A SHIP THAT'S *PRE-SUNK?* THAT'S *ABSURD!*

IT'S AS RIDICULOUS AS... AS TROUSERS THAT ARE PRE-SHRUNK, OR THAT COME WITH RIPS ALREADY IN THE KNEES.

BUT THE POSSIBILITIES...! CONSIDER THIS: IF WE'RE AT WAR, A SUBMERSIBLE SHIP COULD ATTACK A STANDARD BATTLE SHIP--*SINK* IT--WITHOUT EVEN BEING *SEEN.*

STRIKE FROM *HIDING?* HEAVENS, PROFESSOR... WHAT A *COWARDLY* WAY TO DO BATTLE. CERTAINLY NO WAY FOR *GENTLEMEN* TO WAGE A WAR.

AM I THE ONLY MAN WITH *VISION* HERE? AM I THE *ONLY* ONE TO SEE THE TRUE WAY OF THINGS? THIS IS THE VEHICLE OF THE *FUTURE!* ARE YOU ALL *BLIND?*

LOOK, PROFESSOR... I MUST ADMIT, *I* FIND THE WHOLE IDEA REALLY INTERESTING. HAVE *YOU* BUILT ONE OF THESE YET?

ONLY A SMALL, ONE-MAN VERSION...A PROTOTYPE. THE FULL-SIZE VERSION COULD CARRY A CREW OF *TWENTY*. BUT I NEED *MONEY* TO BUILD IT...MONEY I WAS HOPING *YOU* COULD PROVIDE, YOUR HIGHNESS...

THE PROBLEM IS, I DEPEND ON MEN LIKE GRIMSBY AND THE ADMIRAL FOR ADVICE. IF *THEY* DON'T SUPPORT THE SUBMERSIBLE, AND I HAVE THE BIG VERSION BUILT AND TRY AND *FORCE* SAILORS INTO IT...

WELL, PROFESSOR, EVEN A *PRINCE* HAS TO KEEP THE MORALE OF HIS MEN IN MIND. I DON'T WANT TO ORDER THEM TO SAIL A SHIP THAT THEY HAVE *NO* CONFIDENCE IN.

I *DO* SEE YOUR PROBLEM. POLITICS AND ALL THAT. THERE'S *TWO* THINGS I PRIDE MYSELF ON, AND *ONE* OF THOSE IS HAVING RESPECT FOR THE PROBLEMS AND CONCERNS OF OTHER PEOPLE.

TELL ME, YOUR HIGHNESS...

WHAT IF I WERE TO BRING YOU *PROOF* THAT THE SUBMERSIBLE WORKED? SOMETHING FROM BENEATH THE WAVES THAT COULD *ONLY* BE OBTAINED THROUGH THE USE OF A SHIP SUCH AS MINE?

YOU BRING ME HARD EVIDENCE LIKE *THAT*, PROFESSOR, AND YOU'LL *HAVE* YOUR TWENTY-MAN SUBMERSIBLE.

THANK YOU, HIGHNESS. THE OTHER THING THAT I PRIDE MYSELF ON IS ACKNOWLEDGING WHEN I'M IN SOMEBODY'S DEBT.

YOU'VE GOT THE CHANCE. BUT I DON'T KNOW *WHAT* YOU COULD SHOW US THAT WOULD BE HARD EVIDENCE.

I DO.

I SHOULD *NEVER* HAVE AGREED TO DIS!

OH, SEBASTIAN, IT'S GOING TO BE *FINE*.

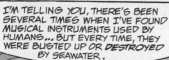

I'M TELLING YOU, THERE'S BEEN SEVERAL TIMES WHEN I'VE FOUND MUSICAL INSTRUMENTS USED BY HUMANS... BUT EVERY TIME, THEY WERE BUSTED UP OR *DESTROYED* BY SEAWATER.

I BET *THIS* TIME WE CAN FIND SOME INTACT, BECAUSE THE SHIP DIDN'T SINK DURING A *STORM* OR ANYTHING, AND BE-CAUSE IT JUST RECENTLY WENT DOWN.

WELL, I JUST HOPE DIS AIN'T A CASE OF CURIOSITY KILLING DA CRAB.

BESIDES, GOING WIT' YOU IS DA *ONLY* WAY I CAN BE SURE YOU'LL BE BACK FOR REHEARSALS ON TIME.

JUMPIN' JELLYFISH!

LOOK AT DA *SIZE* OF DAT T'ING!

AND WE'RE GOING IN *DERE!?*

AW, SEBASTIAN, WHERE'S YOUR SENSE OF *ADVENTURE?*

I MUST'VE LEFT IT BEHIND WIT' MY *COMMON SENSE!*

YOU BEEN ROOTING AROUND HERE FOR HALF AN *HOUR*, YOUNG LADY. ENOUGH IS MORE DAN...

AH! SEBASTIAN! *HERE'S* SOMETHING!

IT HAS BLOWHOLES AND THINGS LIKE THAT. IT *HAS* TO BE SOMETHING MUSICAL.

HERE. *TRY* IT.

EEEWWW!

Ahhh... NEEDS WORK, SEBASTIAN. A LOT.

YOU ASK ME, HUMANS KNOW NUTTING ABOUT PRODUCING DECENT MUSIC! LETS GET OUTTA HERE.

BUT THERE WAS SO MUCH MORE LEFT TO *EXPLORE*, SEBASTIAN!

DON'T TRY TO SWEET-TALK *ME*, GIRL. WE GOT PLACES TO GO, AND *I'M* GOING, AND *YOU'RE* COMING WIT' M--

AHHHHHH!!!!

WHAT IN THE SEAS IS THAT?! I...I CAN'T SEE *ANYTHING*!

IT'S A *MONSTER*!!

COME ON! LET'S *GO* WHILE DA GOING IS *GOOD!*

BUT...BUT IT'D BE *WRONG* TO JUST LEAVE HIM TO DIE! AS...AS BARBARIC AS *DADDY* IS ALWAYS SAYING THE *HUMANS* ARE!

WELL, HE SURE DIDN'T HAVE *YOUR* BEST INTERESTS AT HEART.

LEAVE HIM *BE!* HE *DESERVES* TO--

NO. I'M *NOT* GOING TO LEAVE HIM DOWN HERE TO DIE. AND *YOU'VE* GOT TO HELP ME SAVE HIM.

DAT, YOUNG LADY, IS WHERE I DRAW DA LINE! YOU WILL NOT--

I *SAID,* SEBASTIAN, HE'S *NOT* GOING TO DIE AND *YOU'VE* GOT TO HELP ME.

OH. SO YOU DID.

SHE GOT A *LOT* OF HER FATHER IN HER, *DAT* ONE DOES.

RUNNING OUT OF AIR... PINNED... HELPLESS...

OF ALL THE *IDIOTIC* WAYS FOR A MIND LIKE MINE TO MEET ITS END.

WHAT?!

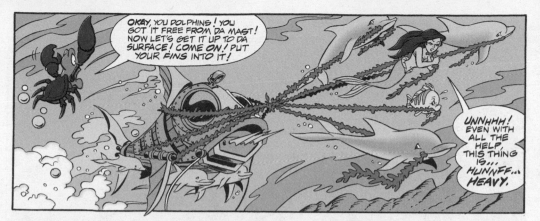

OKAY, YOU DOLPHINS! YOU GOT IT FREE FROM DA MAST! NOW LET'S GET IT UP TO DA SURFACE! COME ON! PUT YOUR FINS INTO IT!

UNNHHH! EVEN WITH ALL THE HELP, THIS THING IS.... HUNNFF... HEAVY.

THIS IS PERFECT! PERFECT!

I HAVE HER IN THE SIGHTS OF THE WIREPOON. SURE, SHE MIGHT BE WOUNDED, BUT AT LEAST I'LL HAVE MY PROOF.

I'LL JUST WAIT UNTIL WE'RE CLOSE ENOUGH TO THE SURFACE... WAIT UNTIL SHE LETS GO... AND...

NOW! NOW'S THE MOMENT! NOW, WHEN--

...WHEN...WHEN SHE'S HELPLESS AND EXHAUSTED...

...EXHAUSTED FROM SAVING ME. AND WHERE'S MY PROUD "GRATITUDE" THEN?

SO, GREAT SCIENTIST... WHAT DID YOU DO NOW?

AND THEN HE JUST SAILED AWAY. I NEVER EVEN GOT A GOOD LOOK AT HIM.

WELL, YOU WERE SURE LUCKY, ARIEL.

DAT'S RIGHT, ALANA, SHE WAS, BECAUSE YOU CAN'T TRUST HUMANS. NOW COULD WE PLEASE GET ON WITH DA REHEARSAL? ARIEL...LET'S HEAR YOUR SOLO.

HEY, WHERE DID YOU GET THAT? THAT SOUNDS LOVELY!

HUMAN BEINGS! HUMAN MUSICAL INSTRUMENTS! I'LL NEVER UNDERSTAND ANY OF DEM AT ALL.

fin

I AM HELPING, MOTHER. LET ME SHOW YOU WHAT I'VE DONE.

DANCE, KHAN! ONE, TWO, LEFT, RIGHT...

YOU SEE? I TAUGHT KHAN TO *TAP DANCE!*

AND HOW, MAY I ASK, DOES THIS HELP WITH OUR WORK?

THIS MEANS WE CAN USE KHAN'S HORSE-POWER TO OPERATE A TREADMILL OR TURN A POTTERY WHEEL OR PUMP THE BELLOWS OR DO ANY NUMBER OF USEFUL THINGS!

MULAN, COME SIT BY ME WHILE I EXPLAIN SOMETHING TO YOU.

SOMETIMES IT IS BEST TO DO THINGS THE WAY EVERYONE ELSE DOES, TO SIMPLY DO WHAT YOU ARE *TOLD.*

I WOULD LIKE YOU TO RIDE TO THE STREAM. TAKE THIS POLE AND TRY TO CATCH A FISH FOR OUR DINNER. DO YOU THINK YOU COULD DO THAT?

OF COURSE, MOTHER...

IN FACT, I'LL ATTACH ANOTHER POLE TO LITTLE BROTHER! THAT WILL DOUBLE THE PROBABILITY OF CATCHING A FISH!

I GIVE UP!

PLOP!

SIT UP QUIETLY, LITTLE BROTHER. SIT.

I STILL CAN'T BELIEVE MY EYES!

THERE'S A WHOLE SCHOOL HERE!

LATER, AT DINNER TIME.

MOTHER! FATHER! I'M BACK!

WERE YOU ABLE TO BRING US A FISH FOR DINNER, MULAN?

WELL, NO, NOT EXACTLY...

I CAME UP WITH A BETTER IDEA. COME AND SEE.

?

I CAUGHT LOTS OF FISH FOR THE FARMERS, AND IN RETURN THEY GAVE US RICE, BEANS, FRUIT AND VEGETABLES, SOME PORK AND CHICKEN AND...

THERE'S ENOUGH FOOD HERE FOR A YEAR.

DO YOU SEE? IT IS BEST TO THINK FOR YOURSELF!

Beauty and the BEAST

Elsewhere

≥Sigh.≤ WELL, *THAT* SETTLES IT. THE WORLD IS JUST NOT *READY* FOR A DEVICE THAT WILL WASH CLOTHES WITHOUT HAVING TO USE YOUR *HANDS*...

Time cannot be stopped but it does flow differently, depending on whether it is measured by the ticking of a clock, or the petals of an enchanted rose...

CAN YOU *IMAGINE!* THE MAN REFUSED TO EVEN *TALK* TO ME! JUST BECAUSE THE MACHINE *RIPPED* UP HIS WIFE'S *DRESS!* I TOLD HIM IT ONLY DOES THAT TO *ONE* IN *TEN* DRESSES! THAT'S A *NINETY* PERCENT SUCCESS RATE!

BELLE! ARE YOU EVEN *LISTENING* TO ME?

I'M SORRY, *PAPA.* I GUESS I WAS-- *SOMEWHERE* ELSE.

THEY HAVE NO VISION! SOMEDAY WE WILL HAVE MACHINES TO DO *ALL* OUR LABOR! MEN LIKE ME ARE *PIONEERS!* IF OUR CREATIONS DO NOT WORK PERFECTLY AT FIRST, IT IS THE *WORLD* THAT MUST BE PATIENT! AN OCCASIONALLY RIPPED DRESS IS TO BE *EXPECTED!*

PAPA? WHERE *ARE* WE? I DON'T KNOW THIS PLACE.

IT'S GETTING *LATE.* I THOUGHT IT MIGHT BE BEST IF WE TOOK A *SHORT CUT.*

THIS LOOKS LIKE *JUST* THE PLACE TO FIND *TROLLS* AND *FAERIES* OR *WITCHES* MURMURING OVER A CAULDRON!

I THINK YOU SPEND TOO MUCH TIME IN THOSE BOOKS, MY DEAR. IT'S ONE THING TO *BE EDUCATED,* BUT IT'S QUITE ANOTHER TO FILL YOUR HEAD WITH *FANCIFUL NOTIONS.*

CAN'T YOU *FEEL IT,* PAPA? THERE'S *MYSTERY* IN THE AIR--AND MAYBE EVEN *MAGIC!* IT'S ALMOST AS IF TIME HAS *STOPPED!*

OH, NO, IT HASN'T! THE *CLOCK* IN MY *TUMMY* TELLS ME *DINNERTIME* IS APPROACHING JUST AS USUAL.

NOW WHERE DO YOU SUPPOSE *THAT* LEADS?

NOWHERE. I MEAN, I DON'T KNOW. NO *ONE* EVER GOES TO THOSE WOODS.

WHY? THERE MUST BE A *REASON!*

SUPERSTITION, I SUPPOSE. I DOUBT THAT ANYONE CAN EVEN REMEMBER *WHY.*

BELLE! *STOP!*

YOUNG LADY, GET BACK IN THIS CART IMMEDIATELY!

I JUST WANT TO SEE ...

...IF I MAKE MY EYES JUST *RIGHT* AND PEER INTO THAT *MURKY SPOT,* I CAN ALMOST SEE SOMETHING THAT LOOKS LIKE A *CASTLE* WITH VINES GROWING UP ALL AROUND IT!

THERE'S NOTHING THERE BUT WEEDS AND DARKNESS! *COME AWAY!*

I'LL JUST BE A MINUTE, PAPA.

BELLE, NO! *DON'T!!*

AN *OWL*! EXACTLY WHAT I *NEED* TO PERFECT MY NIGHT VISION *APPARATUS*!!

NEVER GIVE AN OPPORTUNITY CHANCE TO *TAKE FLIGHT*, I ALWAYS SAY!

GOTCHA!

QUICK, BELLE! GIVE ME A HAND WITH THIS GIGANTIC...

...*BIRD???*

?

I DON'T UNDERSTAND THIS AT ALL. I *KNOW* I HAD IT!

PERHAPS IT WASN'T WHAT YOU *THOUGHT* IT WAS.

WHAT I *DO* KNOW IS I *DON'T LIKE* IT ONE BIT! LET'S GO *HOME!*

YOU'RE NOT *(chuckle)* *SUPERSTITIOUS*, ARE YOU, PAPA?

Heh, Heh. I MIGHT HAVE GOTTEN A BIT CARRIED AWAY.

NOW WHERE ARE YOU *GOING?*

I THOUGHT I SAW-- THERE WAS *SOME-THING*--I JUST WANT TO TAKE ANOTHER LOOK!

BELLE, SUPERSTITIOUS OR NOT, THERE MIGHT BE *WOLVES* IN THERE!

PAPA, YOU KNOW AS WELL AS I DO THERE ARE NO...

...WOLVES IN THESE PARTS!

I DON'T THINK WE HAVE TO ARGUE *THAT* POINT. DO YOU?

IF YOU ASK ME, THIS *ENCHANTMENT BUSINESS* HAS GONE ON *TOO LONG.*

COGSWORTH, YOU ARE ALL *SPROCKETS* AND *SPRINGS!* LOVE CANNOT BE HURRIED AND IT *ALWAYS* HAS ITS DAY.

NEED I POINT OUT THAT WHEN *TIME* RUNS OUT FOR *HIM,* IT EXPIRES FOR *US* AS WELL ?!

NON, BUT YOU WILL, REGULARLY AND INSISTENTLY!

WELL, *SOMEBODY* HAS TO KEEP TO A *NORMAL SCHEDULE* AROUND HERE! ENCHANTED OR NOT, THIS IS A *HOUSEHOLD!*

SACRE BLEU! ARE YOU SUGGESTING THAT *I* DO NOT DO *MY JOB?* IT IS I WHO CARRIES THE *TORCH!*

YOU'RE *DRIPPING WAX* ON ME AGAIN!

IT IS AN *IMPROVEMENT,* I ASSURE YOU!

OH, BOY! ARE YOU GUYS GONNA *FIGHT?*

THIS IS *MORE LIKE IT!* LET'S HAVE SOME *ACTION!*

YOU TWO ARE BEHAVING MORE LIKE CHILDREN THAN SERVANTS WITH *RESPONSIBILITIES!*

IT'S AN *IMPROVEMENT,* MAMA! DON'T *SPOIL* IT!

I...MAY HAVE BEEN--*ahem*-- A BIT **HASTY** WITH MY REMARKS.

MY COMMENTS, TOO, WERE NOT TERRIBLY **BRIGHT.**

TEND TO YOUR **DUTIES**, GENTS. THIS HOUSE IS **BIG ENOUGH** FOR THE **TWO** OF YOU.

WE COULD SURE USE SOME **EXCITEMENT**, THOUGH!

IT IS SILLY TO FIGHT WITH ONE ON WHOM ONE **DEPENDS** SO MUCH.

SO GOOD OF YOU TO SAY SO. **IT IS TRUE** THAT WITHOUT **ME**, THERE WOULD BE NO SCHEDULE TO KEEP!

I WAS REFERRING TO **MOI**, MONSIEUR! IT IS I WHO PROVIDE THE **SAVOIR-FAIRE!**

HARRUMPFF! I HAVE TO KEEP TRACK OF EVERY **SECOND** THAT GOES BY!

THEY GO BY **WHETHER** YOU COUNT THEM **OR NOT!**

IT'S... IT'S... **NO USE!!**

YOU ARE **INSUFFERABLE!** I'LL HAVE YOU KNOW MY PATIENCE IS NOT **WITHOUT LIMIT!**

PERHAPS YOU WOULD LIKE TO STEP **OUTSIDE?!** **CHOOSE YOUR SECONDS, MONSIEUR!!**

NOW, NOW, GENTS...

THIS IS NOT THE **TIME**, COGSWORTH, NOR THE **PLACE SETTING**, LUMIERE. LET'S NOT FORGET LITTLE **VESSELS** HAVE BIG **EARS!**

AW, GEE, IT WAS JUST GETTING **EXCITING!**

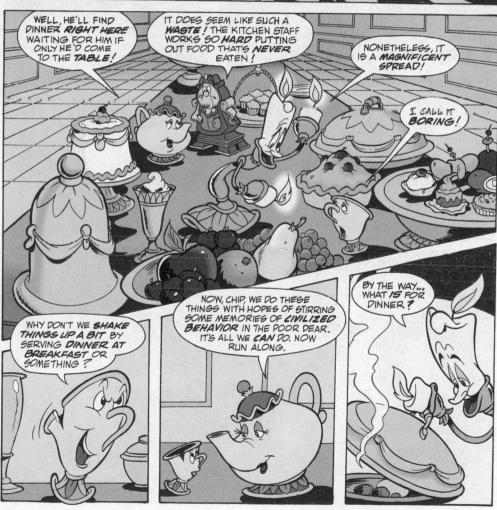

THE *MASTER!* HE'S NOT *BACK!* HE'S OUT THERE SOMEWHERE IN THE *STORM!*

THIS IS OUR *CHANCE* FOR *ADVENTURE!* WE GOTTA GO OUT THERE AND *FIND* HIM!

HI---YO, FOOTSTOOL!!

MAYBE THIS *WASN'T* SUCH A HOT IDEA!

I WOULDN'T KNOW *WHERE I'M GOING* EVEN IF IT *WASN'T* RAINING! WE'D BETTER GO BACK!

OWROOOOOO!

WUFFF!!!

FOOTSTOOL! GO BACK TO THE *CASTLE* AND GET THE *OTHERS*!

DON'T *WORRY* ABOUT A *THING*, SIRE! I HAVE EVERYTHING *UNDER CONTROL*!

ALL WE HAVE TO DO NOW IS *WAIT* FOR SOMEONE WHO *KNOWS WHAT TO DO* ...

DO YOU *REALIZE* WHAT--?!

OUI! QUE! OUI! QUAND??!!

WOOF! WOOF!

Mon Dieu! HE IS *DRIPPING WET*!

WHAT ON *EARTH* DO YOU MEAN BY CAUSING THIS *INFERNAL DISTURBANCE*?!

YIP YIP YIP! WHIIINE!

733

I GUESS THAT MAKES US *EVEN!*

THUD!

PERHAPS NOW WE CAN GET BACK TO A *NORMAL ROUTINE* AROUND HERE.

I KNOW *I* CANNOT TAKE MUCH MORE *EXCITEMENT!*

* SIGH * SOMETHING TELLS ME WE HAVEN'T SEEN THE *END* OF IT YET...

THERE'S A PARTY HERE IN AGRABAH! EXCITEMENT IN THE AIR! MERCHANTS POURING IN FROM NEAR AND FAR... WITH THEIR CARAVANS A-FULL OF WARES!

Disney

Aladdin
and the KING of THIEVES

STEELY MEN KEEP UP THEIR GUARD!

AND SEVERAL CUNNING ROGUES PREPARE...

RUMBLE!

NEVER HAVE I SEEN THE STREETS SO FULL OF *BUSTLE* AND *HUSTLE!*

OUR *PRINCESS* IS TO BE *WED* TO A NO-ACCOUNT *STREET RAT!*

NO WAY! TRY IT *PHONETICALLY...*

IT'S *A-L-A-D-D-I-N!* JASMINE AND ALADDIN ARE GONNA HAVE A *WEDDIN'!*

POOF!

THERE'S A *PARTY* HERE IN AGRABAH, AN' THE *LOOT* IS POURIN' IN!

I *LIKE* THIS WEDDING STUFF SO FAR! MAYBE IF I'M *PLEASANT*, I'LL GET TO KEEP A *PRESENT?*

LAST LOAD OF TASTEFUL FLOWERS...CHECK! THAT'S *EVERYTHING*, SULTY-BOY!

BUT... BUT...

WHERE'S THE GROOM?

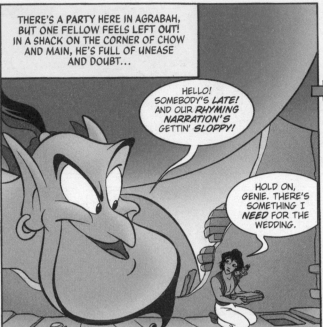

THERE'S A PARTY HERE IN AGRABAH, BUT ONE FELLOW FEELS LEFT OUT! IN A SHACK ON THE CORNER OF CHOW AND MAIN, HE'S FULL OF UNEASE AND DOUBT...

HELLO! SOMEBODY'S *LATE!* AND OUR *RHYMING NARRATION'S* GETTIN' *SLOPPY!*

HOLD ON, GENIE. THERE'S SOMETHING I *NEED* FOR THE WEDDING.

NICE DAGGER! A BIT *SHARP*...

IT BELONGED TO MY FATHER!

YOUR *FATHER?* YOU NEVER SAID A *WORD* ABOUT YOUR *FATHER!* I GOTTA TELL THE CATERER...*CHICKEN* OR *SEA BASS?*

HE'S *NOT COMING.* HE *DIED* A LONG TIME AGO. I NEVER KNEW HIM.

SORRY...

MAYBE IF I *DID* I'D FEEL *READY* FOR THIS! NOT LIKE--A STREET RAT! STEALING WHAT I NEED TO SURVIVE...

LIVING MY LIFE *ALONE!* I'M TAKING A BIG STEP TODAY...INTO A *NEW WORLD!*

WHAT DO *I* KNOW ABOUT *FAMILIES?* GENIE, WHAT IF I'M NOT *GOOD* AT IT?

IF MY FATHER WERE HERE--

HE'D BE AS *PROUD* OF YOU AS *I* AM!

POOF!

AND HE WOULDN'T *LIKE* YOU *SAD!* CHIN UP, AL, YOU'RE GETTING *MARRIED!*

IN A HOVEL NEARBY...

CRUNCH

CRACK!

⤙*GRAR!*⤚

WHY DO *YOU* WALK IN THE OPEN WHILE *I* SUFFOCATE LIKE AN ANIMAL?

SOMEONE HAS TO KEEP A *COOL HEAD*, SA'LUK!

SOMEONE WILL HAVE *NO* HEAD IF THIS IS ANOTHER *WILD GOOSE CHASE!*

⤙*HMPH!*⤚ THE *ORACLE* IS THE *REAL* THING! *THIS* TIME I'M *SURE!*

AH!  OOH!

W-WELL... WE'RE *HERE!*

YES! SOON WE'LL BE TOGETHER *FOREVER!*

IT'S *ALL* SO *MAGICAL!* I'M *NOT* GONNA CRY! I'M *NOT!*

SUDDENLY...

RUMBLE!

ROOMPAH!

RUMBLE!

LET *ME* BE THE POINT MAN! *HYAH! HYAH!*

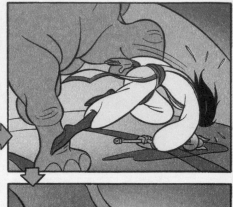

CRASH!

!

!

ROOMPAH!

HRONK!

SNORT!

HEY! WHERE'S THAT "KING OF THIEVES?"

RUMBLE!

I'LL SEE YOU *AGAIN*, BOY.

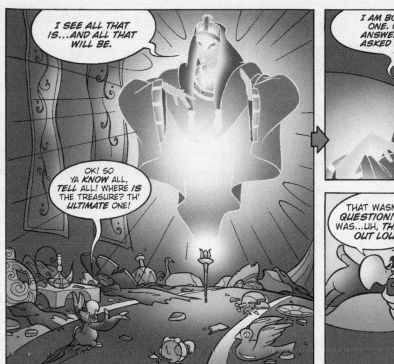

I SEE ALL THAT IS...AND ALL THAT WILL BE.

OK! SO YA *KNOW* ALL, *TELL* ALL! WHERE *IS* THE TREASURE? TH' *ULTIMATE* ONE!

I AM BOUND BY THE RULE OF ONE. ONE QUESTION, ONE ANSWER. YOU HAVE ALREADY ASKED YOUR ONE QUESTION.

THAT WASN'T A *QUESTION!* THAT WAS...UH, *THINKIN'* OUT LOUD!

VERY LOUD!

ALADDIN! WE COULD LEARN ABOUT OUR *FUTURE!*

MY FUTURE IS *YOU.* BUT MY PAST IS A *BLANK!* I HAVE NO IDEA WHERE I COME FROM.

YOUR QUESTION IS YOUR CHOICE. BUT REMEMBER THE RULE OF ONE.

BUT MY PAST IS A *MILLION* QUESTIONS.

AH, BUT ONE MORE QUESTION ABOUT YOUR PAST CAN BE ANSWERED BY YOUR FATHER.

MY FATHER?! M-MY *FATHER* IS *ALIVE?*

ALADDIN! ALADDIN, ARE YOU...ALL RIGHT?

I *ALWAYS* WANTED TO KNOW ABOUT MY FATHER. BUT NOW I'M NOT SO SURE.

WHAT KIND OF MAN *LEAVES* HIS SON? DID HE *CARE*? IS HE *WORTH* KNOWING?

IT ISN'T TOO LATE TO *FIND OUT*. OUR WEDDING CAN *WAIT*.

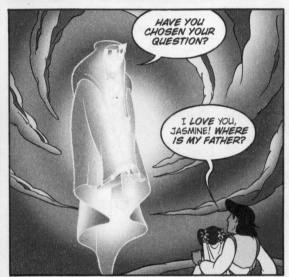

HAVE YOU *CHOSEN YOUR QUESTION*?

I *LOVE* YOU, JASMINE! *WHERE IS MY FATHER*?

FOLLOW THE TRAIL OF THE FORTY THIEVES. YOUR FATHER IS TRAPPED WITHIN THEIR WORLD.

H-HOW LONG HAS HE BEEN THEIR PRISONER?

I AM SORRY...I CAN ONLY ANSWER...

...ONE QUESTION...

SKREEE EEK!

ADVENTURE HO! ALADDIN EMBARKS ON HIS QUEST...

WHOOOSH

~AWRK!~ *I* SHOULDA STAYED HOME WITH GENIE! *MANUAL LABOR* BEATS *DANGER* ANY DAY!

SUDDENLY...

WHOA, CARPET! THE *THIEVES!*

SCREEECH!

THEY HAVE *NOWHERE* TO GO! THEY'RE JUST...*STANDING* THERE...

OPEN SESAME!

AND THEN, BEFORE ALADDIN CAN SAY "BROTHER, THAT'S ACTION!"...

RUMBLE!

FLOOSH!

THE SEA *SPLITS!* THE DOOR *OPENS!* ONWARD!

WHINNY-Y!

RUMBLE!

CLOPPITY-
CLOPPITY-
CLOP

I THINK I'VE JUST *LOST* MY VERY LAST MARBLE.

HANG ON, THE DOOR'S *CLOSING*...

...AND THE WATER'S *UNSPLITTING!*

SLAM

WHOP

YOWOOTCH!

WE COULDA HAD *ALL* THAT LOOT, BUT WE FOLLOWED THE *KING'S PLAN*...AN' GOT *NUTHIN'!*

~OWIE OW OW!~

THE *KING!* WITHOUT HIS *MASK,* HE LOOKS LIKE... LIKE...

YOUR *TIME* DRAWS TO A CLOSE, CASSIM!

CASSIM? MY *FATHER?!*

I DON'T SEE *YOU* SPILLING MY *BLOOD,* SA'LUK!

THEN LET ME *OPEN* YOUR EYES.

!

RUN! I'VE GOT HIM!

I'M *ALADDIN*...AND YOU'RE MY *FATHER!*

~HNGH!~

GROWR!

CLANG!

I DON'T KNOW ABOUT *FATHER,* YOU BRAT! BUT I'LL *SEND* YOU TO MEET YOUR *OTHER* ANCESTORS!

LET HIM *GO*, SA'LUK. THE BOY... *IS MY SON!*

I GAVE THIS *DAGGER* TO MY WIFE YEARS AGO. I TOLD *HER* TO GIVE IT TO OUR NEWBORN SON...*ALADDIN!*

THE *KING OF THIEVES* HAS A *SON!*

YOU'RE THE KING OF THIEVES...

LIKE IT OR NOT, BOY, WE'RE *BLOOD!* I THOUGHT I'D NEVER SEE YOU AGAIN.

BLOOD OR MUD, THE BRAT IS AN *INTRUDER!* AND WE HAVE *RULES* ABOUT INTRUDERS!

SA'LUK IS *RIGHT!*

HE HAS *SEEN TOO MUCH!* HE MUST *DIE.* THEY *ALL* MUST DIE!

MERCY! MERCY!

YES, CASSIM...*MERCY* WOULD BE LIKE *YOU.* SOFT AND *WEAK!* I WOULD MAKE A *BETTER* KING OF THIEVES!

...

KILL THE INTRUDERS!

OR THE BOY *COULD*... NO...

WHAT? WHAT?

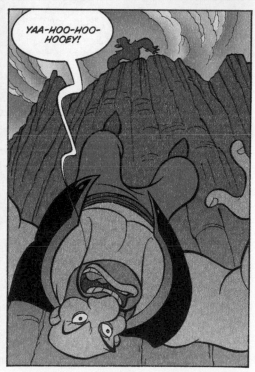

LOOK! I...I...I DIDN'T MEAN...

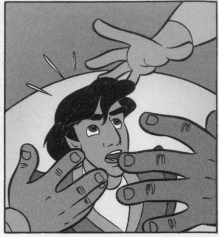

CONGRATS! YOU'VE JOINED THE CLUB! *WELCOME TO TH' FORTY THIEVES!*

!

OUR *CODE* IS VERY *CLEAR* ON THIS POINT. YOU'RE *IN!* YOU *KILLED* SA'LUK.

OR DID HE?

~SPLUT~ TWENTY-SIX YEARS AGO, *AESOP* SAID TO ME, "NEVER TRUST A THIEF!" AND *I* DIDN'T LISTEN!

I'M GOING BACK TO AGRABAH! WE'LL *SOON* SEE WHO ENDS UP *KING* AROUND HERE!

SPEAKING OF AGRABAH, THE NEW PAVILION IS READY...

AND I THOUGHT *I* WAS BLUE!

-:SIGH!:- *NO ALADDIN!* I HOPE HE'S *OK.*

LISTEN TO GENIE! YOU GOTTA GET YOUR MIND OFF THIS *INCESSANT* WAITING!

WHAT'S A *SUREFIRE* WAY TO CHEER UP A *BUMMED-OUT BRIDE?*

POOF!

A *MAGIC* WEDDING PLANNING SESSION!

POOF!

URF?

SEE? THINKIN' *BIG* HERE!

THINKIN' *PRINCESS-Y* HERE!

THINKIN' *SYNERGY* HERE! THE MARKETING GUYS *LOVE* IT!

THANK YOU, GENIE, FOR...*CHEERING ME UP!*

MEANWHILE...

I FIND MY SON AND LOSE AN ENEMY! YOU DID YOUR OLD MAN *PROUD!*

I WAS JUST TRYING TO STAY ALIVE!

HA! IF YOU *DIDN'T* FIGHT, YOU WOULD HAVE BEEN *KILLED!* SO SAYS THE CODE OF THE FORTY THIEVES!

IT'S A *STRICT* CODE, BUT THERE'S ONE THING *I* ADDED-- WE *NEVER* HURT THE INNOCENT!

NOW COME! HERE'S A ROOM MY MEN DON'T KNOW ABOUT!

YOU SEE...THERE *IS* A TREASURE! COMPARED TO *THIS*--A *PHAROAH'S* TOMB IS A PAUPER'S GRAVE!

TH-THE *ULTIMATE* TREASURE?

THE *HAND OF MIDAS,* BOY! AN *AMULET* THAT TURNS ALL TO *GOLD!* AND I'M *SO CLOSE* TO IT!

BUT IT'S ON THE *VANISHING ISLE*...AN ISLAND THAT'S *NEVER* IN THE SAME PLACE TWICE!

HOLD UP! THE HAND OF MIDAS IS JUST A *MYTH!*

NO! IT WAS ONCE *RIGHT HERE!*

THERE'S YOUR *PROOF,* BOY! FROM STEM TO STERN...*ALL* OF IT, *SOLID GOLD,* TOUCHED BY THE HAND OF MIDAS!

AND *SUNK* BY IT.

YOU DON'T *UNDERSTAND.* YOU DON'T KNOW WHAT IT'S LIKE TO HAVE *NOTHING,* TO STARE AT THE PALACE AND *KNOW* YOU DESERVE MORE.

YOU DON'T KNOW WHAT IT'S LIKE TO BE CALLED, "STREET RAT."

YES, I DO.

I KNEW EXACTLY WHAT I WANTED FOR MY FAMILY... THE *BEST!* I *COULDN'T* GIVE UP AND GO BACK EMPTY-HANDED!

NOT TO *YOU.*

BUT WEEKS TURNED INTO *YEARS.* I RETURNED TO AGRABAH ONE NIGHT AND COULDN'T FIND MY WIFE OR SON. I THOUGHT YOU WERE LOST *FOREVER.*

AT THAT MOMENT I WOULD HAVE TRADED *ANYTHING* TO GET YOUR MOTHER BACK!

WE NEVER WANTED GOLD! I WANTED A *FATHER*...STILL *DO.*

COME TO MY WEDDING! THIS TIME YOU *HAVE* AN INVITATION!

I...I JUST DON'T KNOW...

DAD, I'M NOT GOING BACK TO AGRABAH UNTIL MORNING! AT LEAST *THINK* ABOUT IT?

IT JUST WOULDN'T WORK! I DON'T *BELONG* IN *HIS* WORLD!

NEITHER DOES THE *ORACLE!* IT BELONGS TO TWO ENTERPRISING TREASURE HUNTERS... *YOU* AN' *ME!*

THE *ORACLE.* IT'S PROBABLY JUST ANOTHER *DEAD END.*

NO, IT *WORKS!* THAT'S HOW THE KID *FOUND* YOU! IT *KNOWS* EVERYTHING!

EVERY-THING?

AND *I* KNOW WHERE HE *STASHED* IT! YOU *GOTTA* COME TO AGRABAH! IT'S AN *OPPORTUNITY* FOR *US!*

THERE'S A FATHER HERE IN AGRABAH AGAIN AT THE PALACE! ALMOST AS IF FOR THE FIRST TIME...

AL! YOU'RE *BACK!* AND YOUR *FRONT.*

LOOKS LIKE YOU'VE GOT EVERYTHING READY, *GENIE!*

POOF!

NO BIG CROWD *THIS* WEDDING! SECURITY'S *TIGHT!*

I'D LIKE TO SEE *ONE* OF THOSE FORTY THIEVES GET WITHIN AN *INCH!*

WELL! ALLOW ME TO INTRODUCE...

THE *KING* OF THIEVES!

~AAAK!~ ALL UNITS-- WE HAVE A *CODE RED!*

...MEET MY **DAD.**

NO.

SPOOFT

-:AHEM:- AL, DON'T YOU THINK WE OUGHTTA **LOSE** THE **AGRABAH'S-MOST-WANTED** LOOK?

HMM...AS LONG AS HE'S **HERE**...

WANTED!

KING OF THIEVES

POOF! ONE MAGIC **DISGUISE JOB** LATER!

MY BOY ALADDIN MUST HAVE BEEN BORN UNDER A LUCKY STAR...

...TO FIND SUCH A **TREASURE.**

YOU ARE MOST **DEFINITELY** ALADDIN'S FATHER!

IT MUST HAVE BEEN **DREADFUL**... **TRAPPED** BY THE FORTY THIEVES!

UH...

I TRY TO **BLOCK OUT** THE MEMORIES.

SAY NO MORE! NOT **ANOTHER WORD** ON THE SUBJECT!

-:HEH:- NICE SAVE, **DAD!** NOTHING COULD **POSSIBLY** GO WRONG **NOW!**

SOON...

RASOUL, WHAT IS THE *MEANING* OF THIS?!

DAD!

YOUR MAJESTY, MEET THE *KING OF THIEVES!* WE SEIZED HIM IN THE *TREASURY.*

HE WAS AFTER THIS... *AGAIN.*

NOW I KNOW WHY YOU *REALLY* CAME BACK!

YOUR FATHER IS THE THIEVES' *LEADER?* DID YOU *KNOW?*

I...

THOUGHT I COULD *CHANGE* HIM. I *HAD* TO TRY...

YOU CAN CHANGE MY *CLOTHES,* ALADDIN...

...YOU *CAN'T* CHANGE WHO I *AM.*

FATHER, ISN'T THERE *ANOTHER* WAY?

I'M AFRAID THERE IS *NOT!* TAKE THE PRISONER TO THE *DUNGEON...*

...FOR *LIFE.*

THAT NIGHT!

THE ORACLE WAS *RIGHT!* MY DAD *WAS* TRAPPED IN THE WORLD OF THE FORTY THIEVES!

TRAPPED BY HIS OWN *GREED.*

EVERYTHING WAS *PERFECT* BEFORE HE CAME INTO MY LIFE!

I JUST WANT THINGS THE WAY THEY *WERE.*

GENIE, I NEED MY FATHER'S CLOTHES.

C'MON! FOR *WHAT?*

HMM!

TONIGHT THE KING OF THIEVES WILL MAKE HIS MOST AMAZING ESCAPE *EVER...*

JINGLE

...*OUT* OF MY FAMILY.

CLICK-

CLACK!

DAD, I'VE COME TO SAY...

...GOODBYE.

!

ONE QUICK HORSE-THEFT LATER!

HYAH!

~HUFF~ DID WE LOSE 'EM?

THEY WON'T PICK UP OUR TRAIL 'TIL DAYLIGHT! BY THEN WE'LL BE LONG GONE!

WE'LL BE?

THE MOMENT THEY SAW YOUR FACE, YOUR LIFE IN THAT CITY WAS OVER.

I HAVE TO GO BACK! JASMINE'S THERE.

KID, IT'S DONE. YOU'RE A CRIMINAL NOW!

BUT WE HAVE THE ORACLE! THE TREASURE'S JUST WAITIN' FOR US!

IAGO, I WON'T BE--

~GASP~ YOU HAVE THE ORACLE?!

I HAD NOTHING LEFT TO LOSE!

YES, YOU DID.

YA SEE, I--

GO WITH HIM, IAGO. GO.

YA MEAN IT? REALLY?!

SOON, BACK IN THE LAIR OF THE FORTY THIEVES...

I KNOW THE TREASURE'S *LIMITLESS*, BUT I'M NOT CRAZY ABOUT A *FORTY-WAY* SPLIT!

OH?

IF IT WAS JUST...UH, *YOU* AN' *ME*...

I WOULD *NEVER* CUT MY MEN OUT OF THE DEAL! THEY'RE MY *FAMILY!*

...MY *ONLY* FAMILY.

I CAN ALWAYS COUNT ON THEM.

THAT'S WHAT YOU THINK, CASSIM!

WHAT THE--

YOU!

AYE! MY NAME IS *SA'LUK SANDWORM!* YOU *KILLED MY GOOD NAME...*

HOME AGAIN, HOME AGAIN!

FRANKLY, MY BOY, YOUR ACTIONS WERE *MOST* DISAPPOINTING.

THE STREET RAT HAS *OBVIOUSLY* FOLLOWED IN HIS FATHER'S CRIMINAL FOOTSTEPS!

I *OBJECT,* YOUR HONOR--

NO! *MY* TURN.

POOF!

SULTAN, I *CONVINCED* MY DAD TO COME HERE! IT WAS *MY* FAULT.

ALADDIN!

YOU FOUND YOUR FATHER... A FATHER WHO RISKED HIS *FREEDOM* TO SEE YOUR WEDDING.

AND *YOU* RISKED EVERYTHING TO *HELP* HIM...

...JUST AS *I* WOULD FOR *MY* FATHER!

YOUR FATHER? -AHEM- WELL, UH...

LET US PUT THIS MATTER BEHIND US! WE HAVE *POSTPONED* THE WEDDING *LONG ENOU*--

?!

AWK!

IT'S *SA'LUK!* HE'S NOT *DEAD!* HE'S *BACK* AN' HE'S GOT CASSIM!

!

SPLAT!

HIGH ABOVE!

PITY I DIDN'T FIND THIS PLACE *YEARS* AGO. THIS WOULD BE EASIER IF I WERE YOUNGER...

IT *PAYS* TO HAVE A *JUNIOR PARTNER!*

THE *HAND!*

BE CAREFUL! DON'T *TOUCH* THE *GOLD* PART--

HA-HA-HA! *HEADS UP,* DAD!

AT LAST!

I HAVE WAITED *AGES* FOR THIS DAY!

SOON...

C'MON, DAD! AFTER ALL THESE *YEARS*...

...YOU *FINALLY* HAVE YOUR TREASURE!

THIS THING? NO.

IT'S *YOU*, SON! *YOU* ARE MY ULTIMATE TREASURE!

I'M JUST SORRY *THIS* WRETCHED THING ALMOST COST ME YOUR LIFE!

THE HAND OF MIDAS CAN TAKE ITS *CURSE* TO THE *BOTTOM* OF THE SEA...

EH?!

?

!

CLUNK!

BY HUBAL! THE *HAND OF MIDAS!*

LOOK! *GOLD! SOLID* GOLD! TOO *SOLID?*

YES! AT LAST THE MOMENT HAS COME...

HOORAH! HUZZAH!

YOU, OUT IN THE OPEN?! NO MASK? PRETTY RISKY!

EVEN A WANTED MAN CAN RISK A BIT TO SEE HIS OWN SON'S WEDDING. SO, YOU LITTLE TURKEY...

...COME TO SAY GOODBYE?

NAH! I ALREADY SAID MY GOODBYES!

YOU'RE NOT GOING TO LIVE IN THE PALACE?

WITH THE NEWLYWEDS?! IT'LL BE ALL LOVEY-DOVEY! I'D RATHER KEEP MY WILL TO LIVE!

WELL, I DON'T KNOW WHERE I'M GOING. BUT YOU'RE WELCOME TO COME ALONG FOR THE RIDE...

The End

THE CHRISTMAS SPIRIT

Walt Disney

CHRISTMASTIME IN ATLANTICA! AS ALWAYS DURING THIS SPECIAL SEASON, SERENE BONDS OF FRIENDSHIP AND WARMTH RULE THE LAND...

I. S 31

OR *NOT*, MON!

ARISTA, YOU *ARE* THE SUPREME *KLUTZ!*

→PFFT!← *YOU'RE* NOT THE *BOSS* OF ME!

AND *I* WORE THIS BEAUTIFUL *HAT*...

"...AT ADELLA'S THIRD BIRTHDAY!"

ALL THESE *MEMENTOS*! THIS IS *YOUR* SECRET GROTTO, DADDY!

ER...NOW, NOW! JUST A PLACE WHERE I FIND *PEACE* IN TIMES OF *TROUBLE*!

YOUR MOTHER ALWAYS HAD WORDS OF WISDOM ON THAT...

...ESPECIALLY WHEN IT CAME TO *YOU*.

I'VE BEEN AN AWFUL *BRAT*, ANDRINA!

JOIN THE *CLUB*!